818.5

VOLUME SEVEN OF THE

YALE EDITION OF THE

UNPUBLISHED WRITINGS OF

GERTRUDE STEIN

under the general editorship

of Carl Van Vechten

with an advisory committee of

Donald Gallup,

Donald Sutherland,

and Thornton Wilder

THE YALE EDITION OF THE

UNPUBLISHED WRITINGS OF GERTRUDE STEIN

Two: Gertrude Stein and Her Brother

Mrs. Reynolds and Five Earlier Novelettes

Bee Time Vine and Other Pieces (1913–1927)

As Fine as Melanctha (1914–1930)

Painted Lace and Other Pieces (1914–1937)

Stanzas in Meditation and Other Poems (1929–1933)

Alphabets and Birthdays

ALPHABETS AND BIRTHDAYS

BY GERTRUDE STEIN

with an Introduction by Donald Gallup

NEW HAVEN: YALE UNIVERSITY PRESS, 1957

London: Oxford University Press

© 1957 by Alice B. Toklas.
Printed in the United States of America by
Vail-Ballou Press, Binghamton, N.Y.
All rights reserved. This book may not be
reproduced, in whole or in part, in any form
(except by reviewers for the public press),
without written permission from the publishers.
Library of Congress catalog card number: 57-10153

CONTENTS

by Donald C. Gallup

The winter of 1939–40 was a trying one in many ways. For the first time since World War I, Gertrude Stein and Alice Toklas were spending the season away from Paris and, as in 1915–18, there were war and its rumors to make life anxious and exciting. It was naturally difficult for Miss Stein to plan any extended serious work at such a time, and in a period of grave crisis for France it was to be expected that she would respond to the suggestion that she write in her lighter vein her portrait of Paris, France, so intimately bound up with the daily life which she and Alice Toklas were living at Bilignin. *Paris France* was completed in December 1939. ". . . since that is finished except for an ode for [Robert Bartlett] Haas' engagement to be married," she wrote to W. G. Rogers, "I have been like the fields lying fallow and cutting wood . . ."

With the coming of spring to the valley of the Ain, the fireplaces no longer had to be supplied with fuel and Gertrude Stein began to work again on her much rewritten novel *Ida*. As a relief from the seriousness of the struggle with the problem of identity, she began a child's book, "a birthday book I would have liked as a child, more than I would have liked "The World is Round" (as she later described it in a letter to Mr. and Mrs. W. G. Rogers), which she entitled "To Do, A Book of Alphabets and Birthdays." Its plan, involving an orderly progression through the letters of the alphabet with four names for each letter, lent itself to intermittent composition, but once begun, the writing seems to have proceeded rapidly. In the middle of May she wrote to Haas (whom she had nicknamed "Bobolink"; he had written her on April 25 that he was having measles and that his marriage would have to be postponed):

> I have just begun and almost done a child's book to give you whooping cough, this one is called To Do, a book of Alphabets

and Birthdays, it will be a little longer than The World is Round
and now I have gotten as far as the letter Q. when I get to R
it will have to be about a little boy named Robert who is called
Bobolink and can't get married because he has the measles, Alice
says the book is very funny it makes her laugh but she says it
is too old for children and too young for grown-ups, so perhaps that is where you come in, anyway I write a lot of it and
it is almost finished that is I am at the letter Q not quite yet
really half through P. it's really lots of fun . . .

By the 26th of May it was done and she wrote to Haas on June
4:

. . . the child's book To Do has gone off, it turned out to be
quite long over 70 pages typewritten and you come into [it]
you and your measles, I have sent an xtra copy to Carl [Van
Vechten] and asked him to send it to Rogers after he is done
and then it is to go to Thornton [Wilder] and you and Sammy
[Steward] and Wendell [Wilcox], each one as it is easiest to
send it from one to the other as you all come in to the book,
I think it an xciting book and I am most anxious to know what
it is . . .

The question as to what the book is was never definitely answered. Carl Van Vechten was skeptical and tended to agree
with Alice Toklas that it might prove to be too old for children
and too young for adults. Publishers were inclined to be of the
same opinion and the history of the various attempts to have the
book published is an involved one.

The first copy of the manuscript had been sent at once to
John G. McCullough, editor for William R. Scott, Inc., publisher of The World Is Round. Through some confusion about
the address, this manuscript was never delivered and was eventually returned to Gertrude Stein at Bilignin. Meanwhile Mc-
Cullough had borrowed Carl Van Vechten's copy. He wrote
Gertrude Stein after an overnight reading that he felt the book
would be much less appealing to children than the earlier one
because of its lack of episode and the fact that the characters
do not recur with sufficient frequency to hold children's interest. He suggested that she might like either to rewrite it as

purely a children's book or to publish it elsewhere as an older book. Miss Stein answered at once:

> Of course I want it to be a child's story, and to me it has even I might say considerably more narrative and episode than The World is Round, what you say is rather a puzzle to me, however as I say I want it to be a child's book, but I do not want to change it, I do like it the way it is, so consider it carefully and let me hear if you do want it, will you in that case cable me or mail by airmail that you have, in any case as soon as you have decided.

The sequel was described in a letter to Mr. and Mrs. Rogers, written on September 4, 1940:

> . . . and now about To Do I can tell that you did like it, and a funny thing has happened, the editors practically said no and then to my great astonishment day before yesterday, the post office said they had lots of money for me, ah said I, yes they said did you not know, no, I said, well anyway there it was a nice advance and presumably from Scott, I thought it might be Scribner's, I never thought it was Scott although it was the right amount [$250] for Scott and not for Scribner's, and then a cable saying Yes letter follows, I suppose they tried it out on children as is their way and the children in spite of the judgment of their elders said it was a child's book . . .

Actually the money turned out to be from the *Atlantic Monthly* in full payment for an article she had written on life in occupied France, "Mondays and Tuesdays" (printed as "The Winner Loses"). For this she had hoped to get about a thousand dollars.

Scott did not relent, and eventually returned the manuscript to Carl Van Vechten, who submitted it to Scribner's (publisher in America of *Paris France*) and then to Random House, without success. At Gertrude Stein's suggestion it was then placed in the hands of Margot Johnson of the firm of Ann Watkins, the American representative of Miss Stein's English agents. From there it went in turn to the Atlantic Monthly Press, Funk and Wagnalls, Dutton, Simon and Schuster, William Morrow, and finally Harrison Smith.

In March 1941 Carl Van Vechten cabled Gertrude Stein that Smith would publish the book. A contract was eventually signed and an artist engaged to do the illustrations. Here the matter rested when communications were cut off between France and the United States by the war. On September 3, 1943, Margot Johnson wrote Carl Van Vechten that there had been some trouble about the illustrations and that manufacturing difficulties would prevent the appearance of the book before the spring of 1944. There were further complications about the illustrations, however, and Harrison Smith never did publish the book. In 1946 after Gertrude Stein's death, Margot Johnson reported that the script had been lost, and asked Carl Van Vechten for another copy. Mr. Van Vechten replied that plans were being made for including "To Do" in the current series of Miss Stein's unpublished work.

Gertrude Stein's writings for children—the present work, *The World Is Round* (written 1938, published 1939), and *The Gertrude Stein First Reader & Three Plays* (written 1941 and 1943, published 1946)—are particularly interesting because they are composed in a style intermediary between that of such works as *The Autobiography of Alice B. Toklas* and her abstract writings. They afford an opportunity to study some aspects of her method of composition in almost its simplest state. Having for the most part discarded conventional narrative and the useful framework of beginning, middle, and end, Gertrude Stein often found it difficult to start and, having started, to continue. The use in "To Do" of specific groups of names beginning with the various letters provided a device for overcoming this problem. (It is interesting to note that in the original manuscript of the work Gertrude Stein occasionally departed from the strict alphabetical order by going back to an earlier letter. In the course of revision she abandoned this idea, doubtless because it would have proved rather too confusing for children.)

Rhymes and sayings always appealed to Gertrude Stein, and here they come in for frequent use. She was always sensitive to Christian names, and friends and acquaintances appear often among the creations of her imagination. Occasionally, as with Robert Bartlett Haas, an episode is based almost entirely on fact, but usually there is a mixture of actual and imaginary details. George Platt Lynes, like George of "To Do," was a professional photographer who had prematurely gray hair; Carl Van Vechten, like Van, was nicknamed "Papa Woojums" and had and has gray hair and big teeth; but Kate Buss, Wendell Wilcox, Thornton Wilder, and Miss Stein's early school friend Tillie Brown, for example, seem to lend to this piece very little more than their Christian names.

Beyond this illustration of Gertrude Stein's method, "To Do" reflects her concern in her more serious work with certain continuing problems. That of identity, which is at the heart of *Ida*, is at least touched upon in a number of the episodes of "To Do." Her passionate interest in geography and its influence on human beings, stimulated by her visit to the United States in 1934–35, enters into the story of Ursula and her joyous discovery that she was born in the state of Illinois. Generally "To Do" explores the relation of description to imagination in the borderland between fact and fancy.

The child's mind was an ideal place for such an exploration and Gertrude Stein's understanding of child psychology (doubtless based in part upon her early investigations at Radcliffe and Johns Hopkins)—particularly of the child's cruelty and love of violent action, and its logical illogicality—is eloquent in "To Do." In some passages the adult reader may detect higher levels of meaning, but the piece was, as Miss Stein argued, written primarily for children, and she hoped that it would be read and enjoyed by them.

In one of her Chicago lectures Gertrude Stein pointed out that

> I once said and I think it is true that being a genius is being one who is one at one and at the same time telling and listening to anything or everything.
>
> Any of you try it and you will see what a difficult thing it is to listen to anything and everything in the way any one is telling anything and at the same time while you are listening to be telling inside yourself and outside yourself anything that is happening everything that is anything. That is what genius is to be always going on doing this thing at one and at the same time listening and telling really listening and really telling.*

* *Narration* (Chicago, University of Chicago Press, 1935), p. 34.

In "All Sunday," the second piece in this book, listening and telling are almost exactly balanced. Like "To Do" this was the kind of half-fun, half-serious writing in which Gertrude Stein took refuge in time of stress. Just after the first Zeppelin raid on Paris Miss Stein and Miss Toklas had decided to leave the city and go to Spain. After a few months there, they went on to Mallorca and decided eventually to stay the winter. References in "All Sunday" to their having been there a month and a half, and at the end to their having taken a house, date the composition pretty well as the summer of 1915.

Gertrude Stein is concerned about France and the war in general, and this worry constantly intrudes, providing an underlying theme contrasting to the brighter gayer notes of everyday events:

I cannot help thinking of war. . . .

Italy is in the war. . . .

Will Spain come in. . . .

All America is solid for the allies. . . .

We have made a vow never to speak to a german. . . .

You can't be entirely safe when every country is at war. . . .

Eventually of course Miss Stein and Miss Toklas decided that it would be better to be in the midst of things as they happened, and they returned to Paris to work for the American Fund for French Wounded.

Against this background, there is an accumulation of descriptive detail concerning everyday life in Mallorca: walks, letters, dishonest hotel waiters, mosquitoes ("A mosquito is a luminous thing it looks just like a castle in the evening"), religious processions ("Everybody was in the balconies, some were in the street, some were on the side walk, some were indoors we were sitting, we found it very pleasant and they did not boo the governor."), visits to the local powder factory, cock fights ("An example of fighting. An example in fighting is to be pursued, do not neglect speed and pecking, have plenty of Mondays and say if they are in a green box. This seems like

nothing at all but truly it is what we saw."). There are innumer-
able references to food and flowers, to cooks and servants, to
friends and neighbors, even a characteristic comment on her
reading: "I enjoyed the book very much. I enjoyed reading it.
I was glad to see that they were all happy and that they were
miserable those who were capable of spoiling everything." It is
this sense of immediacy, the feeling of looking over Gertrude
Stein's shoulder as she writes, that gives the work its charm. She
frankly discusses her method:

> I am going to tell all my feelings.
>
> Shall it be said that conversation failed and fanning was neces-
> sary and quiet.
> This is the way I am going to write.
>
> I wish to start in this manner. Please me. You please me. Oh I
> can't look in every direction. It is only accidentally that I am
> succeeding so well. What does my hand-writing resemble.
>
> You don't understand me you don't understand the manner of
> my writing, you do see that here and there there is something to
> admire. You are convinced of that.
>
> Seven more chapters and then we will begin something new.

There is a deliberate insertion now and then of a banal rhyme:

> I don't drink water.
> I'm not your daughter.

Or questioning of a homely fact: "Why do stockings come
down in hot weather. There is an explanation. I do not know it."
But there is more magic in such a passage as the following:

> Bicycles are skylarks and a silk night has stars and fish nets are
> bursting, not with fish but with salmonettas. I like frying and
> I will not be willing. More walls have oak leaves. This sounds
> like nothing but they are made out of stones. They would do
> credit to decorations and be witness to a wilderness. Nothing
> wild rests in Palma. Nothing lonely is poisoned. Nothing dis-
> charged is murmured, and loud piles are in the leg. Beat it beat
> coals of it. Have a gloomy tooth. Shape it by the fire. The fire
> has stitches and knows how to sew. By all means be with me.

Walk faster. Like on the ground and see the cows. Have lots
of time. Decide upon a stool. Like soft drinks. Be dazzled.
    What are you doing my precious. Taking grease off my face
my love.

The effect of such a passage perhaps defies analysis, but it is
characteristic of Gertrude Stein's writing at its best.

"A Birthday Book," written between January and March
1924, was the only piece in this volume other than "To Do"
for which publication plans were actually made during Miss
Stein's lifetime. Daniel-Henry Kahnweiler, as he explains in his
introduction to *Painted Lace*, the fifth volume in this series, was
issuing under the imprint of his Galérie Simon in Paris a series
of well-printed books in limited editions illustrated by the artists
whose pictures he handled. When he asked Gertrude Stein for
a manuscript she gave him "A Birthday Book," and for it Picasso
agreed to do the illustrations. Picasso gave some thought to
the project and had actually engraved one plate containing four
subjects which was to be cut for the separate printing of these
four engravings. (The series was to have been based on the signs
of the zodiac "one for each month and two beside . . .") But,
according to Kahnweiler, "Picasso's passive resistance . . .
which shows itself in him, perhaps unconsciously when he is
faced with any commission, any work not spontaneously born
of his own spirit but brought to him from outside—caused the
failure of our project." In 1926 plans for the book were given
up, although two other manuscripts by Gertrude Stein, *A Book*,
illustrated by Juan Gris, and *A Village*, by Elie Lascaux, in due
course appeared.
    In 1927 Gertrude Stein was still nourishing hopes for the
publication of "A Birthday Book." Early in that year she wrote
to George Platt Lynes, who had issued her *Descriptions of Liter-
ature* with a design by Pavel Tchelitchew in May 1926: "I have
been kind of thinking it over and you know I think a very good
idea would be for you to do the Birthday book. You know I
once did a birthday book something for every day it is rather
nice and it could be done very nicely you know a sentiment
on each page and place underneath for baby names, or two on

a page and opposite for baby names, but anyhow it would be like that." For various reasons this plan too came to nothing, and the piece has remained unpublished until now.

In contrast to "To Do," "A Birthday Book," although written for Picasso's son, born February 4 rather than on Gertrude Stein's February 3, could not by any stretch of the imagination be deemed a child's book. It is written in the hermetic style of other works of the period, when Gertrude Stein was experimenting with words and their order and was attempting to divorce meaning altogether from her writing. This might be termed a decorative work, much as one would make a picture through the use of words as elements in a decoration, and it is, I think, clear that Gertrude Stein was principally concerned with the appearance of the words upon the printed page. She had a fondness for the birthday books quite common at the end of the last century—the Longfellow Birthday Book, the Whittier Birthday Book, etc.—in which each day of the year appeared on a separate page, with a blank space for the insertion of the name of a baby born on that day under an appropriate quotation chosen from the writings of the particular poet.

In this piece again, as in "To Do," the name of each day served to bring Gertrude Stein back to reality. The enforced order and progression appealed to her just as the scheme of following the alphabet did later, and "A Birthday Book" is carried through more or less consistently.

The method used is often that of association:

> Fourth of January reminds one of something reminds one of the fourth. The fourth of January reminds one the fourth of January and so forth, and so fourth and January. More January. More slowly. More slowly fourth more slowly January fourth.

There are easy ways out:

> Fifth no one born.

> Sixth no one born.

or the mere repetition of the date:

> January twenty-second and twenty-second. January twenty-second and twenty-second. January twenty-second and twenty-second.

Occasionally, the possibilities of double meanings and variant spellings are investigated:

> Thirty-one won.

And again we find a dependence upon rhyme, particularly with the ordinals for the various days:

> February third heard word purred shirred heard. Heard word. Who.

or even:

> Thirty days has September April June and November . . .

and:

> May and might hold me tight, might and may night and day, night and day and anyway, anyway as so gay, gayly, gayly misses.

Only on a few occasions does the outside world intrude upon this decorative meditation, and it is difficult to regard it as much more than an exercise with words.

"Dahomy" and its subtitle "As Soft a Noise" should not mislead the reader into expecting descriptions of French Africa or any extraordinary occupation with sound. It was Gertrude Stein's custom during this period to write in the small "cahiers" used by French school children. The one she happened to use for the beginning of this new work belonged to a series devoted to the French colonies and was labeled "Dahomey," with a scene in colors from the history of the colony on its front cover. "As Soft a Noise" was doubtless merely a phrase which Gertrude Stein had heard or had said and liked; it appears and reappears in the work.

Gertrude Stein's description of the opus as a serial is much more indicative of its nature. The device to secure a kind of structure without having a beginning, a middle, and an end was the use of numbers in series or progressions. The outside world occasionally intervenes. The opening sentence refers to Godiva the Ford, and to Goddy, presumably the Ernest Hemingway's son, to whom Miss Stein and Miss Toklas were godmothers, and echoes of daily life do now and then appear. The sequence on four families recalls Gertrude Stein's own *The Making of Americans*, and Oakland, California, brings associations with other places, including Pondicherry, of which Gertrude Stein had been so woefully ignorant on the occasion described in *The Autobiography of Alice B. Toklas*. At a lunch at the Whiteheads' the Bishop's wife had suggested that Miss Stein ask the French government to give Pondichéry to England. "After lunch Gertrude Stein said to me under her breath, where the hell is Pondichéry."

Here the style is characterized by the use of repetition, with slight variations which one finds so frequently in Gertrude Stein's writing early and late. These changes rung on seemingly random phrases, clauses, and sentences constitute the serials which make up this almost completely abstract work.

"Birth and Marriage," written at about the same time as "Dahomy," is closely connected with such other domestic pieces as "A Sonatina Followed by Another" (printed in the third volume of this series), to which it is actually a continuation written three years later. It is somewhat more hermetic than the earlier piece. There are still occasional contacts with everyday life, but the work is, like "Dahomy," an exercise in repetition in serial groups with variations and rhyme. The "birth and marriage" motif is struck again and again, much as the phrase "as soft a noise" is used in "Dahomy."

The setting here is presumably the valley of the Ain, and the landscape has its definite influence upon the writing.

> A landscape formed by the surroundings and suitably featured, the landscape features are these, trees placed fortunately for meadows and places, hills placed favorably and even mountains, mountains placed as favorably and even hills, trees placed favorably and always as the same. The next time for meadows and water and places. The next time as evenly.
>
> Landscape interests us as we have said, for as we have said, for as we have said, landscape interests us as we have said.

"A Diary" gives the impression of being less an integrated exercise than the earlier "All Sunday." Outer reality is too insistent and its intrusion seems in the end to win out. Gertrude Stein is plainly here considering again the problem of narrative and is concerned as all through her writing life with the creation of the eternal present. "A diary is not a line a day book," she writes, but is "A distinct record of events." Again ordinary domestic life with its references to food and cooking and sewing provides the unchanging background. Against this curtain are projected the more or less extraordinary events, not in any logical order in time but usually in a time-past, time-present, time-future contrasting pattern: the rose tree given yesterday by Olga Picasso, today's visit from Bravig Imbs, tomorrow's plans. As Gertrude Stein writes at the end, "There will not be a daily diary . . ."

The names which appear are of course the people whom Miss Stein and Miss Toklas were seeing in the spring of 1927 when this piece was written. The Picassos, Bravig Imbs, Elliot Paul, René Crevel, Eugène Berman, William Cook, Fania Marinoff, Kristians Tonny, Tristan Tzara are all introduced, and the principal events are their visits. "A diary is not relieved from the necessity of lists of roses and peonies also of ribbon and attendance."

The familiar elements of Gertrude Stein's style appear once more. Reality often intrudes as a simple declarative of homely statement: "Bread can be kept endlessly."

"A diary should be," Gertrude Stein observes, "simply be," and if a single motive is apparent, it is this. The piece of writing should exist as a creation independent of its narrative of past, present, and future events and rumors. Here Gertrude Stein is obviously preparing for more important composition.

The final piece in this volume is the latest in time of composition and the most advanced from the point of view of style. Written in 1930, when Gertrude Stein was producing a series of studies in history and grammar and what she termed "historic dramas," it is an attempt to reach some kind of conclusion concerning the meaning of history. There are a number of what

seem to be definite answers to the question, presented as a kind
of recurring pattern.

> History is the learning of spectacular consistency privately
> and learning it alone and when more comes they receive.

> What is history. They make history.

The familiar elements of Gertrude Stein's style reappear.
There are occasional intrusions of everyday life, although they
tend to be rarer than in other pieces in this volume. And there
are passages of lyric nature.

> Think with a minute, a minute is too baby who. An owl is
> a bird And wisely is furred Because it is true I love but you.
> She is winsome as a wicked nightingale. A nightingale means
> everything so does after music. Less is less than lest, lest we
> hear the nightingale. The meadow in which they throw rose-
> bush roots is below. To refuse to be cajoled by in which. Oh
> thank you. . . .
> They will name arches by her. Leaves honey and lavender.
> Leave money for her finding it sunny. Money is a flower.

All in all, this volume presents a cross section of Gertrude
Stein's work and will perhaps serve for some readers as an introduction to the other volumes already published in the series.

TO DO

A Book of Alphabets and Birthdays

(1940)

Alphabets and names make games and everybody has a name and all the same they have in a way to have a birthday.

The thing to do is to think of names.

Names will do.

Mildew.

And you have to think of alphabets too, without an alphabet well without names where are you, and birthdays are very favorable too, otherwise who are you.

Everything begins with A.

What did you say. I said everything begins with A and I was right and hold me tight and be all right.

Everything begins with A.

A. Annie, Arthur, Active, Albert.

Annie is a girl Arthur is a boy Active is a horse. Albert is a man with a glass.

Active.

Active is the name of a horse.

Everybody has forgotten what horses are.

What horses are.

What are horses.

Horses are animals were animals with a mane and a tail ears hoofs a head and teeth and shoes if they are put upon them.

If they are put upon them and then the horses lose them and if any one finds them and keeps them, he has lots of good luck. But now everybody has forgotten what horses are and what horse-shoes are and what horse-shoe nails are everybody has forgotten what horses are, but anyway one day, Active is the name of a horse, a nice horse.

He had a birthday he was born on that day so everybody knew just how old he was, he was born on the thirty-first of May on that day, and then he began to say he was not born on that day he was he began to say he was born on the thirty-first of June, and that was none too soon. He liked to be born later every day. Well anyway, there he was and Active was his name, it was his name now but it had not always been, it had once been Kiki, not that he ever kicked not he and he used then to pull a milk-wagon. Then the war came, Kiki was twenty, twenty is awful old for a horse but Kiki had always had plenty, so even at twenty he was young and tender and pretty slender.

So the soldiers came along and they thought he was young and strong and they took him along and everybody was crying and the milk was drying, but they did take Kiki along and he was he was old but he was young and strong.

Then nobody knew where he was, and he was no he was not gone away nor did he stay but he was at the front where there was shooting and he was pulling a little cannon along, and they did not know his name but he was so young and strong they called him Active and he always came right along he and his little cannon. And somebody wrote to him and he answered I have a very nice man, and they sent the very nice man chocolate and everything so he would give Active some, and he did and everybody liked everything even the little cannon that Active was pulling. That is the way it was. And so Active went right along and some one said to him if you make believe you are not well they will send you home. Can I take my little cannon said Active I like it better than a milk-wagon, I like being Active better than being Kiki who was never kicking. I guess I will stay where I am, Active was answering.

And so it went on, and one day there was no more fighting everything was calm, Active was quiet and warm and everybody was going home. And Active was sent home to the milk-wagon, and the milk-wagon was changed to an automobile and they did not need Active for that, they could only use him for ploughing, and they called him Kiki again but Active was his name and he said he would lose his mane if they took away his new name. Well they all cried like anything, they just all cried and cried and then Active forgot everything and he said ploughing was not so bad, and he could always be glad, and anyway, what was the use of saying anything since everybody did what they pleased with him. So he said he thought an automobile, just one day he said he thought he would be an automobile not a new one an old one and he was one, he was an automobile and an automobile never has a name and it never has a mane and it has rubber shoes not an iron one and finding rubber shoes does not mean anything like finding iron horse-shoes did and that was the end of everything.

Then there is B. Well Annie did get mixed up with B. but naturally enough if you see that B follows A and A comes before B.

B is for Bertha and Bertie and Ben and Brave and a birthday for each one.

B for Bertha the one who was the mother of some children. There were three of them.

Bertie was cross-eyed because somebody when he was a baby always stroked his nose with their finger.

The second was Ben who never said when because saying it made him feel funny and the third was named Brave and Brave was always white with delight.

And so each one had to have one one birthday, nobody not any one can say they just each one did not have to have a birthday, even their mother Bertha had to have one.

B. for Bertha and Bertie and Ben and Brave and a birthday for each one.

Brave who was always white with delight went fishing at night. He always fished at night and that was all right because he had been born in the day and Brave was a funny boy because he was not born on his birthday. Any day could be his birthday because he was not born on his birthday. And so he could fish by night and be white with delight.

That was all right.

He was a funny boy.

To be born all right and not to be born on his birthday.

He was a funny boy.

He had two dirty dogs little yellow ones with lots of hair but no care.

They were called Never Sleeps and his brother Was Asleep.

Never Sleeps and Was Asleep always went fishing with Brave at night. Never Sleeps barked all night and Was Asleep was asleep.

Brave was a rich boy. One day, it might have been his birthday because he was not born on his birthday and any day might be his birthday well one day he met the letter A which was a little girl named Annie. Annie was very pretty, anybody could say that of Annie any day and so as Annie was born on her birthday her birthday was the seventeenth of February Brave liked to look at her and so today not Annie's birthday but a day he stopped to say well Annie where are you going today. So then he went on he said you know he said I am rich and strong and you do not need to come along but I am going to give you all my money because you are just as sweet as honey. So he did, he gave her all his money and she took it away and then it was no longer day because night had come, and Brave who was always white with delight went fishing in a river that was flowing and going with all its might. Brave always fished with a light. Nobody should because that dazzles the fish and they cannot see where for the glare so it is not fair. But Brave did he fished at night with a light. And tonight, yes tonight, he was drowned at night, drowned dead at night, and Never Sleeps barked all night and Was Asleep was asleep and Annie had all his money and she spent it on honey, and Brave was never any more white with delight. And the fish could rest every night.

That is what happens when you are not born on your birthday, that is what everybody does say this is what happens when you are not born on your birthday.

Then there is C for Charlie.

Charlie is a boy whose father made chocolate candies.

They all had birthdays.

January.

Oh yes he said and he cried. If I could have a birthday when I tried.

If I could have a birthday beside, January he said January and he cried.

Which one was it.

He did not know which one it was all he knew was that his name was Silly that he had a dog called Billy and that he wished oh how he wished that his birthday, that he had a birthday, say he had a birthday, what day would he have his birthday, oh what day and then there was nothing to say just nothing to say he did not have a birthday.

The first of January.

Nobody knows why he said oh my.

But he did.

Birthday was what he said.

Anyway is what he said.

And his name is Charlie.

That is the real surprise. That, that his name is Charlie.

He did not know it. No he did not. No he did not know it but it was his name. His name was Charlie and January was his birthday, the whole month of January every day in it was his birthday.

Now you can see why he tried and why he cried. So would anybody.

It is nice to have a birthday of January because it comes soon but then again it does not come again.

Charlie had to think of everything.

And yet he could not help it, his birthday, oh dear why try to cry, his birthday, oh dear oh dear oh dear.

January, Charlie, the new moon, and glory.

Birthdays.

D is for Dora David Dove and Darling.

And their birthdays.

Dora knew birds could fly, so did David, but not Dove and Darling, Dove and Darling knew that it was not true, they knew January was taken, no birthday, and February was short no birthday and after that it was too late.

Oh dear said Dove and Darling, no birthdays, not a birthday not one single little birthday.

It is very astonishing about birthdays, some people are born on their birthdays and some are not.

Dove and Darling and they knew it and they knew everybody would know it. Oh dear.

Dove. Love. Shove.

No birthday.

Eight weight late.

No birthdays.

Darling.

Well Darling just thought it would be neat as well as sweet to have one.

All right have one, have a birthday Darling.

Darling was talking to herself. She was saying, have one have one have one.

Nobody knew what she wanted but it was a birthday, of course it was a birthday she wanted, she just had to have one.

And then she heard Dora and David and they were eating fish and they said of course they had a birthday each one had one and what is more they were born on theirs.

Dove let out a big sigh.

She said she would try

To have a birthday oh my.

And Darling said me too

I never was born never at all.

I was never born said Darling,

And Darling was all blue.

Blue is precious said Darling,

And who are you said Dove.

I never had a birthday said Darling, and just then Charlie came along and he said a whole month of birthdays all January only January it came too soon, he would just as leave have been born at noon.

Oh dear said they all

I was born too.

Not I said Dove, I was never born, oh dear and she began to cry and she began to sigh and she began to say oh my.

Well Birthdays are very favorable.

So D comes after C. Just after. C does not care whether D comes after C or not he just does not care. C is C. What difference does it make to C that D comes after C.

But D does care he cares very much that it is such that E comes after D. It makes all the difference to D that E comes after D. Sometimes D says bad words to E says don't come tagging after me, I have had enough of E, let me be. But there it is there is no use in making a fuss E is always there, it is better to be like C and not to care. But D was never very like that, he just could not help being fussed that E was always there, he just could not help being fussed D was and E well E was used to D so he said let it be, no said D no it is not B it is E it is E that I don't want there, well I don't care said E and that was the way it began and D ran and E also ran and Annie had a fan and paper began and A and B and C and D and E were ready to see that nobody came after E. But they did F came after E which was most exciting to see and they hoped it would be a race they ran or to play catch as catch can but not at all, they had to be there at call B after A and C after B and D after C and E after D and F after E. F is in after and that makes it faster. Forget me not.

And so here is E.

Nobody must forget that E follows D. Edith, Edward, Eagle and Eat.

Edith was born late, she was born a month too late.

She should have been born the fifth of June and she thought that was too soon so she was born the fifth of July oh my. So everybody knew the day was wrong so they would not say she was born that day so she just had to get along and she made a song, which said, I am ahead I am ahead, for July is later than June, and the fourth of July would be too soon and here am I not in June but in July, oh my why, but of course I know why, it is because the fifth of July is the day to try to see the sky. Edith always saw the sky. It was a way she had. Others might try to see the sky but she always could even in a thick wood nothing could keep Edith from seeing the sky, and quite right too. Why not. If not. Why not.

The sky is made to look blue.

The sky is made to look pink.

The sky is made to look black.

The sky is made to look blue.

But when Edith saw the sky it was not pink or black or white or blue, Edith could look through and as she looked through she knew that green is not blue, violet is blue, yellow is not blue but black is blue. Anybody else might be confused about the colors of the sky. But not Edith. She knew why. And the reason she knew why was that she was born on the fifth of

July. Birthday or not made no difference to her, she knew why
the sky was blue, why the sky was pink, why the sky was black
and blue. She knew.

There was no use asking her,

She would never tell.

She said for her they rang a bell

And that was because she had not been born in June which
was too soon but in July on the fifth of July oh my.

And she would never tell why.

Never never never tell why.

Eat tried to tempt her to tell.

He knew how very well.

All he had to do was to say well well

And everybody knew that he had everything to do.

Eat was his name and Eat his nature

And he tried to make Edith tell.

But no not even Eat could make Edith tell.

No said Edith no.

Edward and Eagle and Eat said oh Edith tell.

No said Edith no.

And Edward and Eagle and Eat were so excited in getting
Edith to tell that they did not know very well what it was they
wanted Edith to tell. And did Edith know very well what they
all wanted her to tell. No Edith knew she was born the fifth of
July and that she could say Oh my, and that no matter how
much anybody could try they could never make her tell. But
what, well she forgot and so did they, but they never said
What, they were so busy making her tell and she was so busy
saying never never would she tell that they did not know what
it was she was to tell and it was only when they heard something
that was like a bell saying What What What, that they all knew
that it was what they forgot, just what, well what, then what,
What what What.

And so they all went to sleep and it was F. Yes it was it was
F.

But nobody must forget not yet that F follows E. Francis,
Fatty, Fred and Fanny.

Every time Fatty went out he saw a four-leaf clover. That was all there was to Fatty.

But there was lots more to Francis.

Francis, Francis Putz was his name; it is a funny name but it was his name all the same. He liked dogs but he was afraid of them and he liked better talking about birds.

He had a sister who was very tiny, she was only a year younger than he was and he Francis was fair size for his age but she was tiny. In that part of the country all the cats are tiny, there are no big ones and perhaps well it had nothing to do with it of course, but she was only a year younger and her name was Fanny Lucy and she was tiny.

They could play with the ball that belonged to the dog but they could not play with the dog because they were afraid of him. They knew that Never Sleeps and his brother Was Asleep played tag, they saw them, and they knew they played pussy wants a corner, somebody told them that, but and there was no doubt about it, Francis Putz and his sister Fanny Lucy were afraid of dogs and they went on being afraid of them. They were all outside together they and the dogs but Francis and Fanny Lucy always looked away as far as they could from them. Never Sleeps was not really there, they just knew about him, and Was Asleep was taken away so they could not see him. So they settled down to play with Was Asleep's ball. Was Asleep did not mind because he preferred sticks to balls and really Francis and Fanny Lucy did not care much for balls to play with either except just to roll between their legs when they stood with their legs apart and could get somebody to roll the ball under them. Pass through the hole is what they called it. That was what they did. There were no dogs and everything was calm. Just now.

And then they came and they went past them and they went into a house, a man and then a goat and then a woman and then a dog and then the door closed.

Francis knew no one told him but he knew the name of the man and the dog and the woman and the goat and knowing their names just scared Francis. But then anything could scare

Francis. He was the son of a captain and one of his grandfathers was a colonel and the other was a general and just anything could scare Francis.

Goats have no name but men have but Francis never cared what name a man had nor a dog has but a dog does have a name. Francis only remembered his own name, Francis Putz.

Francis was afraid and then he drew a deep breath and then he looked at his sister and he was glad she was tiny because then he did not have to leave her to follow after the man the goat the woman and the dog.

And then it was night.

Nobody knew how that had happened.

Nobody knew.

And it was dark.

And the little sister was not there.

Later they were to say she had walked five miles away.

And she had.

Little as she was she had.

It was dark and it was night.

Nobody knew how it had happened but it had.

It was dark and it was night and there was no light.

It was a funny country, there were mountains but they did not mount, what there really was was a lot of water, and in the middle of the water was a river.

It can happen like that.

The next day it was Friday Francis and Fanny Lucy had a little baby brother.

They sang this song.

Come fire-fly and light up baby's nose.

Come fire-fly and light up baby's nose.

Come fire-fly and light up baby's nose.

Come fire-fly and light up baby's nose.

Then they were all happy together.

Then one day it was Monday they all were lost and there was nothing to eat but grass, so they all ate grass. They knew that grass grew, they knew there were lots of kinds of grass and they did not like any kind that grew.

Well being lost always makes everything yesterday which

was Sunday and so that was the end of that. But yet there were still birthdays.

Francis was born on a day that was frightful because there was an earthquake on that day. Fanny Lucy was born on a day that was awful because it was so hot butter melted, and the baby was better, he was born on a day that was wetter than any other day but still wetter is better than another day.

They none of them ever had another birthday.

And now G comes after F. What did you say I said G comes after F. Anyway it does.

G is George Jelly Gus and Gertrude

Nobody is so rude

Not to remember Gertrude.

George knew all about thunder and lightning but he always sat down.

He sat down when he saw lightning and he sat down when he heard thunder. Not because he was afraid but because he liked to sit down.

He always sat down with a Frown.

That meant that he did not like thunder and he did not like lightning.

He liked to say he did everything as quick as lightning. He liked to say he made a noise like thunder.

That was George.

Funny the way you said thunder and lightning when it is the lightning that comes first not the thunder.

When George was a little boy he went away. Where he went away nobody can say but they never saw George again.

George had grey hair when he was a little boy but that was all right, hair can turn white in a single night and George's did. Whether that made him go away or not who can say.

Before George went away he gave his cat away. He had more than one cat but he only gave one away. That was perhaps because its name was Anyway.

Come here Any Anyway George used to say and the cat came and he followed George about and he never had any doubt that George was George. Then George's hair turned grey and the cat Anyway began to stay away.

Anything can worry a cat and Anyway was worried by that.

If George had had another birthday everything might have been different but he had a birthday on April Fool's day. And he cried when he was born and he said I tried not to be born on April Fool's Day and he cried anyway all day and perhaps he always cried a little every day.

Perhaps that was the reason his hair was grey because he did cry a little every day and he had been born on April Fool's Day.

Anyway he went away and before he went away he gave his cat Anyway away.

His hair was grey and he went away and he was a little boy and his hair was grey and he was born on April Fool's Day and he went away. He was a little boy and his hair was grey and he was born on April Fool's Day and he went away and before he went away he gave his cat Anyway away.

The only thing he took with him when he went away was five rich American cookies. His mother when she made rich American cookies always made twelve of them, they had eaten seven of them and that left five of them and so he took the five of them with him when he went away.

How do you do he said to himself as he went away. Very well I thank you he said to himself as he went away.

Before he had gone far away the five rich American cookies were crumbs and the birds came and took them away, from George whose hair was grey and who was born on April Fool's Day.

George was always next to nothing and he liked photographing. He could not photograph the cookies because they were gone away so he photographed thunder and lightning. First he photographed the thunder and then he photographed the lightning and then he lay down to sleep under a big tree. A big tree does not have roots like a little tree has. A big tree that grows so high that no one can put their clothes on it to dry, has no roots to it like a little tree. It just sits on the ground but it is so big and round that nothing can shake it, even if it does go up high as high as a sky. Think of it and try, a fat boy is harder to shake than a thin boy and George was a thin boy so he shook, he always shook just like a running brook, he shook and shook, that was the reason the rich American cookies crumbled away, that is the reason his hair was grey, that was the reason he was born on April Fool's Day that was the reason he went away and that was the reason he gave his cat Anyway away. He was so thin he was always shaking, and so he went to sleep where the biggest tree that ever grew would be sure to, not to shake. Not even in an earthquake.

Poor George, it was inch by inch that he slept, and he was not even wet, he shook so that no rain could drop on him and he shook so that he was so thin that he could never have a twin.

But let it never be forgotten that he liked branches on trees that were rotten, he was so thin they could not fall upon him, his hair was grey because he was so thin and he went away because nobody could find him he was so thin and he loved thunder and lightning because he was so thin, they could do nothing to him, and so he grew thinner and thinner and his hair grew greyer and greyer and the big tree grew bigger and bigger and three times three made twenty oftener and oftener and the lightning and the thunder grew stronger and louder and the cat Anyway was dead anyway and the rich American cookies were far away, the birds had taken them away and what could George do or say, he could take one photograph a day but that was not enough to pay his way, he had no way to pay, poor George poor dear thin George poor dear thin grey-haired George poor George he was away there is nothing more to say poor dear thin grey-haired George he was a thin grey-haired boy and he had no toy and he had no joy and the lightning and thunder were brighter and louder and the big tree was bigger and he was thinner and pretty soon well pretty soon, there was no noon there never is if you are born on April Fool's Day, there is no noon no noon, and pretty soon and in every way George dear George began to fade away, fade fade away, he was born on April Fool's Day, he was grey, he was thin he went away he knew all about lightning and thunder he was under the biggest of big trees and that was no wonder, George George it was no wonder lightning and thunder George born on April Fool's Day had faded away.

After G is H for Henry.

Henry and Harold and Henrietta and House.

Harold was the last of the Saxon kings.

Henriette de Dactyl, Yetta from Blickensdorfer and Mr. House.

Henriette was a French typewriter Yetta was a German typewriter and Mr. House was an American typewriter and they all lived together, they click clacked together only Mr. House made the least noise.

They were all three machines and they worked every day and they had nothing to say and that was the way it was.

Nature never sleeps.

That is what the little machine the typewriter Henriette de Dactyl said to herself nature never sleeps, but said Henriette de Dactyl I am not nature because whenever they let me alone I sleep, I can always sleep, I wish I could cook cookies, I wish I could plant trees, I wish I could cook mutton chops, I wish I lived on an avenue of cauliflowers I wish I wish said Henriette de Dactyl and then it went click clack and it said nature never sleeps, and it was asleep. Yetta von Blickensdorfer said I am nature because I sleep with one eye one eye one eye, said Yetta von Blickensdorfer and if you only sleep with one eye you can never cry.

These two typewriters were very little ones you could carry them around and Yetta von Blickensdorfer was very proud when they carried her around, she always kept one eye open when they carried her around, even when they put her on a high shelf she never lost herself she always kept one eye open even when the closet door was shut.

Henriette de Dactyl was not like that, she said nature never sleeps but a sweet Henriette de Dactyl sleeps very well, she too would like to live somewhere but she did not want to live on a cauliflower avenue, she wanted to live on Melon Street, and she wanted to eat radishes and she wanted to eat salads and she wanted to eat fried fish and soup. And when they carried her around and as she was a very little machine she was bound to be carried around she always closed both eyes very tight and she always let out little squeaks with all her might, and then she always hoped there would be some light if they put her on a shelf but if there was no light she said it was just right, right without moonlight and she just fell asleep both eyes shut tight.

But Mr. House he was not a mouse he was a great big typewriter, they could not carry him around, they could only cover him over.

That is what made him such a nice lover. They could not carry him around but they could just cover him over.

And so Henriette de Dactyl and Yetta von Blickensdorfer up on their shelf so high both thought they would die if they never saw Mr. House again. They knew they would, and Henriette cackled like a hen, she knew she would die if she did not try to see Mr. House the American typewriting machine again. And Yetta would groan and would moan and she knew she would be like a stone if she never could see never never never could see Mr. House the big typewriting machine again.

And so there they were and everywhere there was no one, and so would they could they did they can they will they shall they sha'n't they can't they might they if they, as they, suddenly they heard a voice say, as you were and there they were as they were.

Terrible terrible day, to be as they were.

Nature never sleeps said Henriette.

Forget forget said Mr. House.

Not yet said Yetta.

And then she felt better.

But Henriette knew and Mr. House too that when the cock crew and the mouse said mew it would be Sunday.

Well very well Monday comes after Sunday.

Gracious me said Henriette, I have not been born yet.

Mr. House said in a solemn voice typewriting machines are not born they are made, and even if they are always in the shade, they are made.

Oui oui, said Henriette oui oui.

Ja ja said Yetta ah.

And Mr. House said nothing more, because he was not a bore and he would have been of course he would have been if he had said anything more.

More More More.

Shut oh shut the door.

It is shut said Henriette.

Not yet said Yetta.

And so the three typewriting machines went to war, they said they would, they would they said.

Henriette fell off the shelf.

Yetta was left there all by herself.

Mr. House quick as a mouse heard the noise, he did not go to help because he thought he heard a yelp and he did, but it was not a fuss, Henriette had fallen off the shelf but she was not a muss, she just said she would fuss and she did, and Mr. House quick as a mouse covered her with his cloth he had one of course it covered him over and so there they were Mr. House and Henriette and it was fair that they were there, and Yetta all alone on her shelf could not take care of herself, she just got dirty and cried and when anyone tried to make her keys go they stuck ever so, and so no, no there was no use, no use in that, she might as well have been a cat, and Mr. House got on very well and so did Henriette who loved to look well when they said she would tell how to fall off a shelf and not hurt herself much, it was such fun to tell every one.

So there it was begun and it was finished before they were done and every one has a gun and no one can run and that is what war is and now there is none, thank you every one.

And I follows H, it does not sound right but it is H and then I it is better to try H and then I, H I makes high.

I is Inca Isaac Irresistible and Inez.

Isaac said that he was better, but was he. Isaac said that he felt better but did he. Isaac said that children should be seen and not heard but should they. Isaac said that eighty was more than four but is it. Isaac said that ink is blacker than blue but is it. Isaac said that bridges are wetter than clouds but are they. Isaac said that water is wetter than dolls but is it, Isaac said that yes is quicker than no but is it. Isaac said that butter is whiter than snow but is it. Isaac said that leaves are red, but are they; Isaac said that he had read that he would be dead if he went away, and said what he had said but would he. Isaac said that it

was better to be red than blue but is it. Isaac said that a clock
would stop if you said what what, but would it. Isaac said that
he met a head and when he met a head he hit it, but did he.
Isaac said that he changed what he said so that it came back to
sit with it, but did it. Isaac said that a chance to wed would
come if he saw some one, but did it. Isaac said that it was all
right that he would stay awake every night but would he. Isaac
said that he felt like lead, but did he. Isaac said that when he
ran he always began but did he. Isaac said not at all, not at all,
and then Isaac said everything is all everything is all and Isaac
said I am very tall but is he.

J comes after I of course it does, it was of course it was J.
Jay, Jay is a bird, a bird that if it comes it eats green peas and
little thumbs. Of course it comes, it is grey and black and wishes
it was all black because then nobody would know it was back
but of course I was thinking of a magpie. But J is other things
it is James, Jonas, Jewel and Jenny, and anybody can ask more.

But and there must always be more than one there must always be four, no more, just four. J is also just, just why, that is
no lie, just why or why, well well.

But after all well well and you can never tell if it is a bell or
if it is just well well. Well anyway, I does come before J. It is
no lie, it does it just does come before J even if there is a J to
pay and there is in just, not in must but in just.

So then to say that I comes before J remember I is Ivy.

Ivy was Ivy, she was Ivy by name and Ivy by nature and she
was born on the fifth of August, what a lovely day to have as a
birthday, the fifth of August, it is so warm it is never cold and
nobody ever needs to be told that it is cold because it never is
cold.

And so Ivy was Ivy by name and Ivy by nature and she was
warm like August and small and round like 5, and there she
was and what happened to her. Well she fell in love with a king.
He was such a pretty king and so she fell in love with him.

There is no use in being a pretty king if a king is a pretty
king well there is no such thing.

And so Ivy fell in love with a pretty king and really there is
no such thing.

But she did she fell in love with a pretty king and he was king and she was in love with him and he was pretty and she was in love with him.

So she said she would sit at home and be in love with a pretty king. And she did she sat at home and she was in love with a pretty king. And it was everything and he was pretty and he was a king and she stayed at home and she was in love with him.

And he came to see her yes he did and he said here I am and she said yes, and he said here I am all the time and she said yes, and he said I am a king and she said yes and she said yes and such a pretty king.

Well up to then he had known he was a king but he had not known that he was such a pretty king. And now she said yes and such a pretty king. Then every one said yes and such a pretty king and then some one said should a king be a pretty king should a king be such a pretty king and soon every one was saying should a king they were saying should a king be a pretty king should a king be such a pretty king, and Ivy said yes, and everybody else said no and the king did not say anything no king ever does, and so one day well it did happen one day he was not a king and he went and saw Ivy who was sitting and he said I am not a king, and she said and such a pretty king, and he said such a pretty king and she said such a pretty king and so they said let us sit down and they sat and Ivy said yes such a pretty king and the king said yes and Ivy said yes and they both breathed tenderness and it was the fifth of August and very warm and it was the day Ivy had been born and it was her birthday and the king did not have one, he had had one when he was a king but now he was not a king he did not have one. But anyway Ivy had one, and when two are one then one is one, and Ivy and the king had begun and they never knew that two are one and the only thing they knew was that the fifth of August was warm. Which of course it is.

And so H. I. J. you have to say h i j to be sure that J comes after I which it does.

There were two brothers and two sisters James, Jonas, Jewel and Jenny, they used to quarrel about which was the biggest, they used to quarrel about which was the oldest they used to quarrel about which was the tallest they used to quarrel about which was the smallest and when they quarreled they used to say that they would take away each other's birthday. And they did that was just what they did, just exactly what they did.

One day each one had taken away somebody else's birthday and at the end of the day not one of the four of them had a birthday, they had everything to say but they just did not at the end of the day they just did not any one of them they just did not have a birthday.

And now they wondered what they should do. There was no use being in a stew, each one had taken the birthday away from the other one and now all four of them had none, because each one as soon as they had taken the other's birthday away they had thrown it away and later on when they all wanted their birthdays back again they went out to find them but they were gone perhaps a duck or a lobster had eaten them anyway all four birthdays were gone not one of them had one.

So they decided to advertise, they said they would pay to have any one give them their birthday back again or if not that one then some other one. But it was funny nobody answered them there evidently were none, no birthdays to give away, and so James and Jonas and Jewel and Jenny had none between all four of them they did not have a single one.

And then they remembered they had heard of them there were the dogs Never Sleeps and Was Asleep perhaps while Never Sleeps was barking and Was Asleep was asleep they might take their birthdays away from them. And they did, they went up very carefully while Never Sleeps was barking and Was Asleep was asleep and they took their birthdays away from them. And really Never Sleeps and Was Asleep would not mind much not even when they found that their birthdays were gone, but and that was another thing, there were four of them James, Jonas, Jewel and Jenny and there were only two birthdays for the four of them and they quarreled more than before and pretty soon they tore the two birthdays in pieces and now there were six without birthdays James and Jonas and Jewel and Jenny and Never Sleeps and Was Asleep and six without birthdays is just six too many.

What was there to do.

And then they were all so tired they lay down to sleep all except Never Sleeps and Was Asleep, that of course, and when they slept they dreamed they dreamed that across a wide river perhaps it was the Mississippi and it was a mile deep there were birthdays to give away every day and so all four, James and Jonas and Jewel and Jenny started to swim across to where birthdays were no loss, of course Never Sleeps and Was Asleep did not try to cross and as they tried to swim across all four were drowned, of course they were drowned they had no birthdays so of course they were drowned and Never Sleeps' and Was Asleep's sleep was sound and the birthdays were never found there were none of them around. And this is the end of a sad story.

So after J comes K. K is easily K, it looks different it is different it is K.

K is Kiki, Katy, Cake and Kisses.

Mrs. misses kisses

Mrs. kisses most.

Mrs. misses kisses

Mrs. kisses most.

Katy, Katy Buss

What a fuss

What a fuss

Katy Buss.

Katy Buss was her name

Katy Buss was her game

Katy Buss was her fame

Katy Buss was the same.

So there now.

How

So there now.

Katy Buss knew how to make cake.

She made it.

Katy Buss knew how to kiss

She kissed it.

Katy Buss knew Kiki Buss.

Kiki Buss knew Katy Buss

And it was ice and it was so
And it was dates and it was snow.
And then actually Katy Buss ate it.
All this sounds funny but it was money.
Money makes makes cakes.
Katy Buss sighed.
It was extraordinary how she sighed
She loved her birthday.
She just loved her birthday.
Her birthday was on the fifteenth.
After that it was on the twenty-first
And after that it was on the first.
Always the same month always the same year and that was
queer.
Necessary but queer.
And now to hear
What Katy Buss has to say.
She stands on a chair which is there.
She leans on a table when she is able
She reads a book which she took
And she made it do who are you.
This is the way it does.
She said does and this was the way it was
She said me and then she put out to sea
She said very well then and she pulled all the feathers off of
a hen
She said might I glide
And she knew what there was beside
And she said today yes today,
Yes today makes yesterday.
Well she said yesterday well yesterday was my birthday.
Everybody was surprised.
They well might be.
And beside
Well anyway there is enough to say and Katy Buss said it.
And there is enough to eat
And Katy Buss ate it
And there is enough to know

And Katy Buss knew it
And there is enough to chew
And Katy Buss chewed it.
Who knows what a cow does.
A cow chews its cud
Who knows what Katy Buss does.
She does and she was.
Was what
Katy Buss.
Oh dear they next to know nothing.
That was what was just as likely.
Next to know nothing.
Katy Buss went purple with joy.
Kiki Buss did it to annoy
And Klux Buss said ahoy.
Nobody came which was a shame,
And just then,
Well very likely it was just then,
Katy Buss flew, she flew right away to kiss her birthday.
For goodness' sakes is what it had to say is what her birthday
had to say but Katy Buss did not mind. She was that kind, the
kind that did not mind.
And it was just next to nothing
But she had her birthday,
All right she had her birthday
All right All right she had her birthday.
All right All right All right.
All right
All right she had her birthday.
And nobody said what.
And she did have it.
She had her birthday.
Which day
The first day.
And what month
The third month
And what year
Any year

Oh dear.
Remember it is queer.
It is of course
Believe it or not it is of course.
And Katy Buss could be cross
And she was.
And that is all there is to that.
L comes after K
Like it or not it does.
L is Lily-Leslie, Let and Up.
Well do you understand that.
This is the sad story of Leslie-Lily.
Lily who always found everything Hilly.
Leslie's little Lily's last birthday.
When he said come she always came
When he said go she always goes
Come come he said and she comes
Go go he said and she goes
And he says come come and she comes
And he says go go and she goes
And it worries her toes
And tickles her nose
But still when he says come come she comes
And when he says go go she goes.
And this is Leslie's Lily's last birthday.

Any hen has a birthday, it does seem funny to say it that way but any hen has a brithday any hen or any chicken or any lily, all this is peculiar.

And any hen and any chicken and any lily has its last birthday. Sometimes they say they will have their last birthday all together, the chicken eats the lily, the lily loves the hen the hen loves the chicken and they all say when and Leslie eats the chicken and the chicken said when and Leslie ate the hen and the hen said when and the lily, the tiger lily, the white lily, the purple lily, the double lily, Leslie's little lily had a last birthday and she did say when.

So it might have been but was it then, the hen was but not the chicken, Leslie was but not the lily, the lily was little and lily white and fat and that, that was what the chicken was the chicken was little and white and fat and he ate Leslie's lily and that was that. So the lily Leslie's little lily had its last birthday.

Its first birthday was hard to see because it did not show it was so slow but the last birthday was easy to see because the lily was always on the go, it hoped for snow but even so it was very easy to know.

Now when was its last birthday. Just what day.

Rather not said Leslie.

By that he meant that he would rather not that the little lily had a birthday. He just would rather not. That is what he meant when he said rather not and he did say rather not.

But the little Lily had a birthday just the same it had no name they just called it a little lily which it was but it had no name not a real name not a name that anybody would know was a name but it had a birthday. You can have a birthday without a name and the little lily had done it it had a birthday without a name and so anybody can understand why Leslie looking down at his hand said rather not.

And then oh deary me what did Leslie see when he looked down at his hand anybody can understand what he did see when he looked down at his hand, he saw he had plucked the lily the fat little lily, the fat white little lily and he had it in his hand.

Anybody can understand.

Oh dear.

M and N are the middle of the Alphabet one one end of the middle and the other the other end of the middle and they have not the slightest idea whether they should look at each other or not. They were never ready, one looked one way the other looked the other way.

And so one way M was Marcel, Marcelle, Minnie and Martin and N was Nero, Netty, Nellie and Ned.

Well which was it said or red.

Which was it.

Well to begin.

Man is man was man will be in.

In what.

In a minute.

Just not.

Not what

Not more than a minute.

Madagascar

Please shut the better part of a half up in a car.

And that is what they meant.

I like it when they think that twenty and twenty make forty.

I do hope that you do.

So listen well.

Marcel is the name of a boy and Marcelle is the name of a girl.

It takes an eye to see that a girl has a double l e and the boy has only one l.

It does take an eye a quick eye or a slow eye but it does take an eye. An ear well an ear is good enough but it is not enough it takes an eye.

Marcel and Marcelle were going to a marrying bee. A marrying bee is where you go to see and when you see you say she will be married to me. Marcelle and Marcel had not seen each other before but when they went through the door he said she for me and she said he for me.

So then they married and they had two children Minnie and Martin.

So then there were four and when the four were there it was time something was happening.

And it did happen.

The birds began to sing

They sang like anything.

And then suddenly they stopped and sat.

And why, because they saw their first bat,

The first bat of the season

A little black bat that was making believe it was a bird just like that.

And so the birds stopped singing and a bat can't sing

So it was the moment for Martin and Minnie to begin.

They did.

In the meantime Marcel the father and Marcelle the mother began to shudder.

It was the bat that made them feel like that the first bat of the season.

And then pretty soon Marcelle the mother and Marcel the father saw a glow-worm and that gave them quite a turn.

So everything was happening and it was evening.

Way up in the sky ever so high was something flying it was not a bird it was not a bat it was not a hat, it was an airplane and that was that.

Please Mr. Airplane take us flying said Martin and Minnie very nearly crying.

But Marcel the father said firmly no, it is better to think than to go, I tell you so.

Martin and Minnie went away they had nothing to say but they knew oh how they knew that it would happen to be true that way up high like a bird in the sky they would fly.

Papa Marcel and Mamma Marcelle had said very well, it is always necessary to say very well and Papa Marcel had been up there once too. Papa Marcel knew everything and he said enough is enough. And Mamma Marcelle knew everything and she said enough is enough but Minnie and Martin they did not know anything and so they said not enough is not enough it is all stuff, we do not know enough not enough.

And so while Mamma Marcelle and Papa Marcel were asleep and dreaming Minnie and Martin were dreaming and they were awake and they said it would be better than cake to sit and swim in the moon and to sit on the clouds and to have curtains for breakfast curtains of sky oh my they said, oh my.

They were not asleep they were dreaming and all of a sudden there it was tumbling an airplane coming and before they knew they were there. And everybody said come out quick, take an umbrella call it a fence open it quickly and down you will come in the fog that is dense and it will be like soup in a minute and later then you will be awake just a minute.

It was very likely that nothing had happened very likely, very likely indeed, it was very likely that it was Papa Marcel and Mamma Marcelle who were awake and dreaming and Minnie and Martin who were asleep and dreaming, very likely. So they had the next day.

And now there was going to be a large party because it was everybody's birthday.

April eighteenth was everybody's birthday.

Everybody liked to be born on the same day so that it was more economical. If the father and the mother and the brother and the sister were born on the same day it is very much more economical, because then the birthday cake can all be made on the same day, the party can all be had on the same day, the presents can all be had on the same day, it is much more economical, and so to be economical Marcel the father and Marcelle the mother and Minnie the daughter and Martin the son were all born on that one, that one same day.

If you think this pleased every one you are mistaken.

It did not.

It did not please Minnie for one.

It did not please Martin for one.

It did not please Marcelle for one

It did not please Marcel for one.

It did not so it would appear if you believe all you hear.

It did not please any one.

But all the same it was done, they were all born on the same day and then what happened. Well what happened what happened was this the eighteenth of April was over before they all were done being born and they were all so worn, so worn out with having been born, that when they heard the birds singing and the bat flying and the airplane whirring, they just gave up they just did, they said they were just worn out with being born, they were not going to have a party or cake or presents or anything, they were just not. And so you see it really was extremely economical because as they were all born on the same day and they were all too tired with having been born all on the same day to go on having a birthday they just did not have anything and that is very economical.

And now the first half of the alphabet is done and the second half of the alphabet is begun.

N is begun

Nero Netty Nellie and Ned.

There are twenty-six letters in the alphabet and half of

twenty-six is thirteen and thirteen is an unlucky number, of course if one cannot help one's self and one is in a hurry to be born and just cannot wait until the fourteenth or if one is always a little slow and could not get born on the twelfth, there is nothing to do but just do what you do that is get born on the thirteenth, and the alphabet being twenty-six letters it has two thirteenths and you can see that they are worried about being unlucky because they got called M and N. Any one pretty well any one would know that M and N are unlucky. You have just heard the sad story of the Marcels and Marcelles and Minnies and Martins and now it is N and there is the sad story of Nero and Netty and Nellie and Ned.

It is very sad, they just could not be glad it is very sad, M is very sad and N is very sad and they just could not be glad and it was of course it was because that alphabet instead of having twenty-eight letters went to work and had twenty-six and the half of twenty-six is thirteen, and halves are always two and so all the way through N and M had to be thirteen and neither of them could be a king or a queen or a bird or a crow or a cow or a hen or a lamp or a house or a cat or a mouse, they just had to be thirteen, they could be nothing in between.

M thirteen N thirteen and thirteen is thirteen and oh dear. Who said oh dear.

Nero said oh dear and Nellie said oh dear and Netty said oh dear and Ned said oh dear and they all said oh dear and they said it again and again.

Oh dear they said oh dear.

And they found it very hard not to always say oh dear. They just always did say oh dear.

Oh dear.

Well there they were Nero and Nellie and Netty and Ned and they were all saying Oh dear.

It was all the fault of the alphabet being twenty-six letters with the half being thirteen.

So said Nero and Netty and Nellie and Ned, so if we have to have N which they say is what it is, and undoubtedly N is what it is well said Nero and Nellie and Netty and Ned since N is

what it is let us just be as wicked as we can let us all be born on
the thirteenth just to go with N that is Nero and Netty and
Nellie and Ned and let us just never go to bed.

They all said yes let us never go to bed, let us never never
go to bed. Let us be born all born on the thirteenth and let us
never never go to bed.

They decided and it was very wise of them to decide to do
this because supposing they had said they would go to bed.
Well supposing they had decided to go to bed, what would
have happened, why they would have all been dead, that is
what would have happened.

Oh dear, what would have happened, it was just that that
would have happened. And so nothing happened because they
did not go to bed.

Little by little each one of them got up instead of going to
bed and they would begin to count and they would say perhaps
there is a mistake, perhaps Monday is Sunday and perhaps
thirteen is twelve, perhaps. And then one of them would slowly
get up, you must remember they had none of them not one of
the four of them not one of them had ever been in bed, and
they would get up and they would say, perhaps they would
say, oh dear, and then they would say, perhaps they counted
wrong, perhaps Wednesday is Monday, perhaps it is and perhaps
thirteen is twenty-five perhaps it is, and perhaps Saturday is
Friday perhaps it is and perhaps N is X perhaps it is.

They just went on perhapsing like this until they almost fell
asleep but they know they had said they would never go to bed
and so what could they do they could get up but they could not
go to bed and so this was what they did do. And so they went
on Nero went on and Netty went on and Nellie went on and
Ned was along and they all made a song.

If Friday was Monday
And Tuesday was Sunday
If Wednesday was Friday
And Saturday was Monday
If Sunday was Tuesday
And Wednesday was Friday

Who would say which was a lucky day and who could say whether there were more than there were yesterday or less than there were Friday.

Who said they, who knows when we were born.

Who knows.

And the cuckoo clock answered.

Who knows.

Who knows.

So said Nero they said clocks talk, they tell time, if we smash all the clocks nobody will know when we were born and we can say we were not born on any day they say. Yes let's, they all said, and they each of them got themselves a hammer and they began to smash clocks, and then some one saw them and said what are you doing. We are smashing clocks said Nero Netty Nellie and Ned, but why was said what have the clocks done, they have said we were born and we were not born we never go to bed we are not dead, and the clocks are always talking and they are always adding and we are tired of listening.

You can see what an awful letter N is, just an awful letter, and then all of a sudden a little clock began, it did not tell the time it made a chime and Nero and Nellie and Netty stopped hammering clocks and they stopped to listen and the little clock said go to bed go to bed, and Nero was sleepy and Nellie was sleepy and Netty was sleepy and Ned was sleepy, and as the little clock kept saying go to bed go to bed, well they did they just did go to bed, and each of them had a little bread and they laid their head on the pillow of the bed and they were not dead and they were asleep and all their troubles were over and they forgot to say oh dear, they said instead how nice it is to be here and that was all there was to it and they forgot the alphabet and they forgot thirteen and they forgot they were born and they were sweetly sleeping thinking they were eating strawberries in the dawn on the lawn.

And that is the end of the sad story of N which is not as sad as the story of M which is much sadder and badder, of course it is.

And now there is O.

O of course could not be sad O could only by glad.

Orlando Olga Only and Owen.

Believe it or not they really had these names. O always makes people like that.

My gracious said Orlando isn't it lovely the wind in the trees.

You mean the green trees said Olga, oh yes said Only the wind in the green trees. You mean said Owen the blue sky and the wind in the green trees. Oh yes said Orlando my gracious isn't it lovely.

Much as they were used to it they could not settle down to sit they had to run to meet some one.

That one said gracious me and Orlando said I said gracious me, and that one said well what makes you think you said gracious me.

Orlando stopped and said I don't know. I did say gracious me. He looked around at Olga and Only and Owen and they looked at him as if they did not know him.

What said Orlando did I not say gracious me. And nobody said anything.

Orlando was puzzled, had he said gracious me, had he said gracious me it is lovely or had he not.

Well anyway it was lovely, the wind in the trees was lovely, the green trees and the blue sky but had he said the trees were green and the sky was blue, had he.

He stood and looked and Olga and Only and Owen looked as if they did not see him.

Orlando began to feel very funny.

Suppose said Orlando I get them away from here will they then look at me as if they did not see me. I wonder.

And slowly Orlando went away and neither Olga nor Only nor Owen followed after.

Pretty soon Owen saw another tree and he said gracious me the wind in the tree is lovely.

And he looked around and he found that Olga was there and she said the green in the tree and Orlando said yes the green in the tree gracious me isn't it lovely and he looked again and there was Only looking at him as if he had seen him, and Orlando said yes the wind in the green tree gracious me isn't it lovely and Only said yes and the blue sky and Orlando said yes gracious me oh my the wind in the green tree against the blue sky isn't it lovely.

And Orlando looked around but Owen was not anywhere around and he said dear me gracious me oh my I could cry everything feels so funny.

So Orlando went away and he had nothing to say and Olga and Only came after and they went away and they could not see that Owen was there too until suddenly they heard a hulla-baloo and there was Owen up in the tree and they could not try to say good-bye because Owen made such a noise there was no reason why that they should try.

So all of a sudden Orlando said I have had enough you all go away, I am going alone, you can go home if you have a home, Orlando began to be very bitter if you have a home, I said Orlando said I am going to try to see if I can see the man who said I did not say gracious me.

So Orlando started off but the others came after, because Orlando was right, they had no home so they had to roam and why not follow Orlando. If you have no home you have to follow and you try to say hulloa but really it is better to follow.

So they started off but Orlando was cross and he would not know they were there.

Well were they there. Olga and Only and Owen.

Orlando said they were not there, they said they were there, well anyway what did they care they none of them had any home to go to.

So they started to see if everywhere the wind was in the trees the trees were green and the sky was blue, and gradually they knew that it was true that everywhere the wind was in the trees the trees were green and the sky was blue, that is nothing new but it is true and they wandered on for they had no home and what is the use of making a moan if you have no home and it is true that the wind is in the trees and the trees are green and the sky is blue.

As yet there was nothing else to do and they had no home.

So Orlando said he had rather be alone, but they said no no they would not go, they would go with him. They had not

meant not to see him when that other one had said that he
Orlando had not said gracious me the wind in the tree. No said
the three they had not meant anything they would follow Orlando. What else could they do, they had no home, no indeed
no home, no home.

It is funny not to have a home very funny but it does happen to a great many. When you say funny sometimes it makes
you laugh and sometimes when you say funny oh my it makes
you cry.

That is what happened to Orlando and Olga and Only and
Owen, they said it was funny not to have a home but when they
said funny oh my it made them cry.

So they began to wonder why, why they had no home and
they knew it was true they had no home. But they had a birthday each one of them had a birthday and if they each one of
them had a birthday well then they must have been born and
if they had been born they must have had a home everybody
can say that there has to be a home to have a birthday and now
oh dear where had it gone away, not the birthday they each still
had one, but the home. The home the home.

So then they began, they could not remember back had they
all had the same home, had Orlando had the same as Olga, had
Only had the same as Owen, they could not remember but they
did not think so and why because as much as they could try
they could not remember always having been together. And
when they were like this they never thought to give each other a
kiss they just thought they would not look as if they knew who
was who.

And so slowly Orlando grew stout, that made it difficult for
him to move about.

And then Olga slowly grew thin, that made it difficult for
her to win any one to come to lunch, she had nothing to eat and
so it was not a treat for her to want any one to come to lunch.

And slowly Only grew long and that was a bother because
beds are short and he was long, he could not stretch out, he had
to put a chair there beside his bed to either put his feet on or
his head. It was not much fun being too long, he never thought
it was funny very long.

And slowly Owen was short, short and shorter until anybody thought he could be bought, kept to show in a circus or
what, well that was not a way he liked to be bought, and so
every day and in every way he got a little shorter and if so and
they bought him to show well in a little while he would go
because he would be too short to see, and that would not be at
all funny.

So there they were, no home, no nothing but each one of
them had a birthday, and pretty soon each one knew that rather
than anything they would like a room, it might just as well be
a moon but a moon was always changing its shape and a room
well a room ought to be always there with a window and a
door and a ceiling and a floor. Finally they knew Orlando and
Olga and Only and Owen that it was the O that made them
go so funny.

So then they said if they could only get rid of the O and
so they tried that way but only Owen could say his name
without the O, he might be called Wen but then if he were
called Wen where was his birthday, his birthday was for Owen.
The others just could not say their names without the O, just
try it and you will see that is so, so having no home they just
each one of them was on the go all night and all day, which any
one can say is not a pleasant way.

So then they thought they would collect stamps. They had
to do something so they just thought they would collect stamps
and if they collected enough stamps they might find one that
would lead them home.

This was not much of a success. Orlando liked to lick stamps
but he did not like to keep them, Olga hated stamps, Only liked
stamps but he could not read and Owen he was always the best
of the four and sometimes he thought if he only was not with
them somebody would take him to a home and he would not
have to roam.

Well that did happen to Owen, somebody said little as he
was they would take him they liked him little only he would
have to have a new birthday and begin again well would he.
He thought and thought and all he could say was well would
he.

Well would he.

This is all there is about it, well would he.

And then there was Orlando, he was so stout he could not get about and so he stayed where he was and if you stay where you are long enough then that place gets to be your home. Well that was all right for Orlando only he was so large he did not have birthday enough to go around, so he thought he might as well go and get drowned. But if you are very stout you cannot drown, so what could he do, he had to have a birthday and he was so stout that his birthday could not get all about him. Oh dear what could he do. What could he.

Well what could he.

And then there was Olga she was so thin that she had not place enough to win being her home, she was thin she could not fit in and so it could not be her home, so she said she would she would stay, but did she, if she did her birthday would be a bother to her because birthdays have to be able to see the one whose birthday they are and Olga was so thin the birthday could not see her, so would she get out to try to be stout and keep her birthday, now would she.

Now would she.

And now there was Only and Only was so long, all along Only was so long he was so long all along that he was all along because he was so long.

So how could he have a home and a birthday, would the birthday be in his head or in his feet, and would either his head or his feet be a treat for his poor birthday. His poor birthday said every birthday oh dear.

And so Only would only hear oh dear, and his feet would only hear oh dear, so what did Only do.

Now what did Only do.

What did Only do.

So you see this is the end of O's and who knows when you say it is funny it will make you laugh or cry, oh my.

And now there is P.

P is really funny.

Peter Paul Pearl and Pancake.

Peter's birthday was the first of January.

Paul's birthday was the second of February.

Pearl's birthday was the third of March and Pancake's birthday was the fourth of July.

It just did happen that way they did not try but it just did happen that way.

Peter was an old man, he had a daughter and she had five children. Peter lived far away and so on the first of January all five children had to write him on his birthday. They did not say but they felt that way why did he have to have a birthday and they did not say but they felt that way and they did say why did he have to have a birthday the first of January. It was not very convenient naturally, in the first place there was Christmas and he was far away and it was almost Christmas Day and they all five had to write to him on his birthday. They had not yet their Christmas gifts so what could they say, what could anybody say to a grandfather far away on his birthday the first of January when they had not yet had Christmas candy. Oh dear. It was queer but there it was, it had to be done, and before the setting sun, the sun was setting and not any one of the five of them had even begun the letter to their grandfather on his birthday. Well there they were all five of them and each one had to write a different one, and they had such lovely paper their mother had given to them, and they had such lovely ink and such lovely pens and never a thing to say to grandfather so very far away. To be sure they had never seen him but they knew his name was Peter and their mother she said he was sweeter than any one and he sent them nice presents when they came but dear me they had not come.

So there they sat and they were not allowed to chat and their mother came in to see them begin. Not one of them had begun, not one, they had said dear grandpapa, each one had said dear grandpapa and then they were done.

So the oldest said mother darling mother, give me the first sentence the first sentence is such a bother, and then with that one I can go on like anything. So the mother said all right, I will show you how to begin. And me and me, cried each one, so she gave each one a beginning and then she went away singing.

It did seem so easy to write what she had told them and they stopped, how could they go on, well just how could they go on. Tomorrow was coming and the sun was setting and if they had thought of anything they would certainly be forgetting but they had not thought of anything to forget no not yet.

And so they sat and they looked at the cat and the cat went out into the setting sun and oh dear me their letters were only just begun.

So their mother came in again to see how they were getting on. Oh dear dear mother they all said, our pens are as heavy as lead, what do we say next, we have all begun, see how we have all begun but what do we say next. Well what did they say next, she had to tell each one something they said next and then she said now only work and you will be done and she went away into the setting sun.

Oh dear the sun was setting more and more, you could see it on the floor and not one of them could think of anything more oh dear oh dear oh dear if only there was an open door. But there was none. Well there they were and it was almost night and their mother came in to see if they were all right. Well they were all right, if you call it all right to know you would have to stay there all night to make the letter go right. Not one of them had written anything, they just could not think of anything to say to their grandfather far away and on his birthday.

So it seemed it was almost the next day but really it was only a little while when their mother was back to see what a pile they had been writing. Well there it was, it was just as it was, each letter was just as it was and all five of them were sitting. Oh mother dear they said it is very clear that if you would only tell us how to end then it would be a wonderful letter we would send, oh mother dear do tell us how to end. So the mother told each one what to say to make it done and they did and that was that and they felt they felt they could get a hat and go out in the clear night and have a pleasant fright and how they had done everything in the way that was right and with all their might.

The moral of this story is the grandfathers who are far away should not have their birthdays on the first of January, they had much better choose another day for their birthday.

P. Peter Paul Pearl and Pancake.

Paul was not a grandfather, he was a grandchild and he was wild he was so spoiled and he just thought every day was his birthday just any and every day because he was spoiled that way.

He thought everything was a theatre performing just for him, his grandmother his mother and his father and he could mimic every one, he could make believe he was a chauffeur waiting for his mother, he could make believe he was a girl who had robbed her brother, he could make believe he was his own grandfather, he could make believe he was a beggar, he could make believe he was a boy who had lost his mother, he could make believe he had been run over, he could make believe he was frightened and would change his home for another, he could make believe that he had a sister and that he had lost her and had found another, he could make believe anything and his father said he would send him away to school but he was so spoiled the school would not keep him so he was home again making believe everything.

One day he made believe that fourteen was twelve. He made believe it was, then he made believe that five was three, he made believe it was, then he made believe his home was burned down he made believe it was and then he made believe that a girl he knew had forty dogs. When he made believe this girl he knew had forty dogs he made believe that all forty followed him, they followed him all forty of them and they ate everything all forty of them and they bit every one all forty of them and Paul made believe they would go on biting every one and eating every one until there would be nothing or not anything left alive any more anywhere. While Paul was making believe this thing he made believe that the forty dogs would always do whatever he told them and he made believe he was telling them to kill everybody and everything and then he made believe that he would make the forty dogs kill each other and bite and eat them and then he Paul could make believe that he was the only one living and that everyday was his birthday.

But while he was making believe this thing the forty dogs turned on him, they bit him and he ran away, he did not make

believe running away he just ran and ran and ran away and
that was the end of him.

Pearl was not like him at all, Pearl was a girl.

When she knew who was who, she was astonished too.

It astonished her to know she was a girl.

Who are you they asked her and she said she was Pearl.

And what is pearl they said to her, and she said Pearl is a
girl.

Every time she said Pearl is a girl she was astonished.

That is the kind of a girl Pearl was.

She was the kind that is astonished.

She was astonished by everything.

She was astonished when she went in bathing.

Water astonished her, everything astonished her and what
astonished her most was everything. She was like that.

So then she decided to go on being astonished. And so the
first thing that happened to her she decided was very astonishing. And what was that first thing that was happening. Well the
first thing that happened to her was to be born and that certainly was very astonishing.

She just was astonished. There she was, she was born and
her name was Pearl and Pearl was a girl and it was all very
astonishing. It certainly was.

Then the next thing that happened to her was to have a
birthday and that was certainly an astonishing thing to say, Pearl
was a girl and she had a birthday. She was so astonished she just
stopped everything but everything astonished Pearl that was
the kind of a girl Pearl was.

You would suppose that she would get used to being Pearl
and to Pearl's being a girl but not at all it rolled along like a
ball this being astonished by everything.

Supposing she got up in the morning, well she found the
morning astonishing and when she went to bed at night well
you might say she was not very bright but she did find the bed
and the night very astonishing.

She found her head astonishing and her feet and her hands
and her hair. She did not care, she just would say what she
thought and she did think it was astonishing she thought it

was all astonishing. That was the kind of a girl Pearl was Pearl was that kind of a girl she found everything astonishing.

And then she met Pancake, that was his name Mr. Pancake. Now you might have supposed that she would find that astonishing that his name was Mr. Pancake and that she met him but not at all, she did not find him astonishing at all, she just ate him and after that, well after that, well it made her feel funny to have eaten him and after that well after that nothing was astonishing, that was the kind of a girl Pearl was, she was that kind of a girl.

Q is Quiet, Queenie, Quintet and Question.

It is hard to have names like that. Very very hard, it makes anybody troubled to have names like that, very very troubled but all the same they had them.

Mr. and Mrs. Quiet

Miss Queenie

Mr. Quintet

and Master Question.

The night was all around them and they were wondering if it was thundering and very likely it was.

That is the way Mr. and Mrs. Quiet were, they were always wondering whether it was. They had rabbits no hens, they had goats no boats, they had sheep no lambs and they had no cows, they had leaves no grass and they had bread no cake and they were always awake. That was the kind of husband and wife Mr. and Mrs. Quiet were. They had tongues and no teeth, they had knives and no forks, they had spoons and no bread, they had no hair on their head, that is the kind of a couple Mr. and Mrs. Quiet were.

Once in a while they had potatoes, once in a while they had cabbage, once in a while they had wood to chew and once in a while they drank water. Once in a while. They led a very happy life Mr. and Mrs. Quiet.

They had a bicycle but they did not ride it they pushed it and on it they put their cabbages when they had them and their potatoes when they had them and behind them went their goats and at home were their rabbits and they were very comfortable every day that is what they did say Mr. and Mrs. Quiet.

They had a favorite rabbit Mr. and Mrs. Quiet and he was the only rabbit they had who had a birthday. He was a very big rabbit a very bad rabbit and he had the habit of always eating a little rabbit on his birthday, a very very bad habit, but Mr. and Mrs. Quiet could never quiet that habit it was the habit of this rabbit. And they thought, one day they thought that if they made believe that he was caught and that they would tell him what they thought of this habit of eating a baby rabbit on his birthday that it would cure him, but it did not, on his next birthday he went back to his habit of eating a baby rabbit.

So they thought Mr. and Mrs. Quiet thought of taking away his birthday and in that way he would be cured of the habit of eating a little rabbit on his birthday.

Well what happened.

Nothing and then it was a terrible thing, they took away his birthday and so he did not know what day was his birthday so just to be sure he ate a little rabbit every day just as if every day was his birthday. He was a ferocious rabbit and Mr. and Mrs. Quiet did not know what to say, there he was eating a little rabbit every day.

Mr. and Mrs. Quiet did not know what to say if they let the rabbit run away, well they tried that but he wanted to stay he just would not run away and they could not kill him and eat him because after all he was their favorite rabbit. Then they decided to get the best of him, they gave away every rabbit they had, just gave them away and then when it was the big rabbit's birthday he looked around for a little rabbit to eat on that day, and there were no little rabbits they all had been given away. So he refused to eat anything, he was mad and he refused cabbages and carrots and everything, he would not eat anything he was just mad. And Mr. and Mrs. Quiet did not know whether to be sad or glad and then they decided to be glad. The next day the big rabbit refused to eat anything, it was not his birthday but he refused anything even on an ordinary day because he had not had a little rabbit for his birthday. So there were Mr. and Mrs. Quiet looking at the big rabbit and the big rabbit looking at them and the eyes of Mr. and Mrs. Quiet were full of tears they were worried like anything about

the big rabbit and the big rabbit's eyes grew redder and redder
he had begun by having pink eyes but he had eaten so many
little rabbits on his birthday that his eyes grew redder and redder
and then an awful thing was happening, the big rabbit's eyes
grew redder and redder and Mr. and Mrs. Quiet who were
looking at him found him more and more alarming and then
all of a sudden the big rabbit's red eyes burst out into flame, the
big rabbit was on fire inside him and he and the cabbages and
carrots he had not eaten were all flaming and the smoke and
fire were coming out of him and the little house he lived in was
burning and Mr. and Mrs. Quiet who were looking at him found
it all terrifying, they were so frightened they could not do anything, they could not get any water to put the fire out they were
so frightened they could not move about and so they just sat
there watching and pretty soon it was over the burning there
was nothing left of the big rabbit but a red cinder and that Mr.
and Mrs. Quiet put out by dropping tears on him. And after that
Mr. and Mrs. Quiet lived very quietly with their goats and
everything but they never after had another rabbit.

Miss Queenie and Master Question and Mr. Quintet never
had anything like that happen to them. They never had cared
not any of them for goats or rabbits or anything. What they
liked was fish in the morning, beef at noon and eggs in the
evening. That is all they cared about. Miss Queenie said it made
her stout to eat trout, Master Question said that beef gave him
indigestion and Mr. Quintet said he always when he saw an
egg he Mr. Quintet always said not yet. And still what was
there to do, there was fish in the morning, beef at noon and eggs
in the evening and the more often it was happening the more
often Miss Queenie said trout in the morning made her stout
and Master Question said beef at noon gave him Master Question indigestion and Mr. Quintet said whenever he saw an egg
he Mr. Quintet said Not yet.

And so they thought they ought to think of something so
they thought and they thought that they ought each one of
them to think of something. So then they thought that if each
one brought something they would not have fish in the morning

beef at noon and eggs in the evening. But what could they bring, anybody could ring but what could they bring.

So they said we could give each other something. Now we do not know said they when it is each other's birthday, so let us play that any day is one of each other's birthday and then we could bring something for that day. Yes they would say but then say today which one of us will get what we bring and which two of us will bring, on a birthday others bring but the one who has the birthday he gets everything, well now how, how can we know which will bring and which will get everything.

Naturally a thing like that would mean quarreling. Miss Queenie, she being a girl and she knew she was a pretty girl at least she said she knew she was a pretty girl because she had a curl, well anyway she said they should do the bringing and she would do the receiving, but not at all said Master Question, that is out of the question, to be sure you are a girl and you may have a curl perhaps yes perhaps no it is only you who tell us so, but I I who am always in question, I who have indigestion, I will receive everything to decide what part I will keep and what I will divide, and beside said Master Question it is my right to have a birthday because I am so bright every day.

Then Mr. Quintet said Not yet Not yet, Mr. Quintet always said Not yet, he said Not yet, he said do not let no he said do not let any one think that it is not for me to decide about how to divide everything. I am Mr. Quintet, that means there are five of me yet and so you bet I will not let any one divide anything.

Well there they were they could not decide not about birthdays or anything so they just went on, and there was fish in the morning and beef at noon and eggs at night, and Miss Queenie said trout in the morning made her stout and Master Question said beef at noon gave him Master Question indigestion, and Mr. Quintet said eggs at night, when I see them all right I always say I Mr. Quintet I always say Not yet.

So they all three live on very unhappily and they never decided anything about their birthday.

You have to say the whole alphabet almost to get to R because Q always throws you out. Now everybody knows that.
So there is R, R rolls around and around like a ball not that it
is a ball not at all. R for Robert, Redbreast, Rachel and Rosy.

Rose had a dog a little dog named Chilly.

Chilly was his name and chilly was his nature.

That is in winter, in summer it was another matter.

In the summer he was as mad as could be.

Rosy said to him remember Chilly how cold you were in
the winter.

But Chilly said no it is summer and I will kill everything,
you see you just watch me.

And Rosy did she just watched Chilly and she saw that one
thing led to another and then to one thing more.

Chilly began by barking at his dinner. He barked very hard
at his dinner. Then he ate his dinner. Then Chilly began of course
this was summer he began to be warmer and warmer and one
thing followed after another. He saw a chicken and he thought
a chicken with its feathers on must be hot, so he went after it
like a shot, and it was too big to kill, not that really Chilly would
want to kill it, but he did want it to be still so he could take all
its feathers off until there would be no feathers on it, and it
would be nice and cool and perhaps would go swimming in a
pool.

Rosy tried to save it but Chilly wanted to shave it shave all
its feathers off by pulling them out of course, and so he did and
Rosy was cross because everybody would say that they would
take Chilly away and everybody would be cross of course,
cross with Rosy because Chilly was such a little silly, it was
Rosy's fault of course.

And so Rosy tried to take Chilly away from the chicken
where it lay and then Chilly decided to play it was a mouse's
birthday. He did play that it was a mouse's birthday, five little
mousies were born and Chilly said there would not be any
harm in running after the mother mouse now that the little
mousies were born, so he chased the mother mouse away and
later in the day he found her again and what shall I say, well
Chilly made away with the mother mouse that day, the day the

little mousies were born and even though it was warm the little mousies born that day never had another birthday.

And this was a day of Rosy's little dog Chilly whom everybody said was silly but he was not at all silly, and in the summer he was not chilly, no it was Rosy who was silly to let Chilly do whatever he wanted to. But they just went on every day, Rosy and Chilly and in the summer when it was warm Chilly did a lot of harm, not really very much harm because he was so little and that is what Rosy always said, she said let him alone in the winter he is so chilly let him do what he likes when he is warm, and so they did and so Chilly did, and Chillys do and so do Rosys and in the winter they sit by the fire and wink and think of what they did in the summer and what they will do another summer and so there they are and is it fair to mousies and chickens that they sit there by the fire and stare Chilly and Rosy, but perhaps yes and perhaps no, well believe it or not it is true that is what Chillys and Rosys and chickens and mousies will do.

Robert was a boy well he was grown up now and yet he was not bigger than he had been, when he said when had I been, and they said do not tell him but call him Bobolink and that will make him think that he is bigger yet. Not yet said Bobolink.

When they called him Bobolink it made him think of Miss Robin-Red-Breast.

Bobolink had a mother and she said Robert, when I call you Bobolink what do you love best.

Robert went pink he said when you call me Bobolink I love Miss Robin-Red-Breast best.

So Bobolink tried to get married beside, to get married to Miss Robin-Red-Breast, his bride, but he couldn't and why, it will make you cry, he couldn't because he caught measles.

Imagine that, his mother was there and she said take care, if you think of Miss Robin-Red-Breast all day perhaps you will get that way, spotted red and right there ahead of Robert called Bobolink was measles and measles is red oh dear said Bobolink if my hair had been red, my measles could not spread, oh dear said poor Bobolink.

But he had measles and he had to stay in bed all day and he had to stay awake all night and everybody gave him something all day, well that was perhaps like a birthday. Sometimes measles does take you that way.

So he went on having measles every day and so he could not get married that day, of course nobody ever got married having measles nobody, and then it was the fourteenth of February, it was Saint Valentine's day and surely said Bobolink surely those naughty measles will go away.

But they didn't, they looked as if they were going to stay they acted as if they were going to stay they talked as if they were going to stay and it was no use for poor Bobolink to tell them about Saint Valentine's day and how he was to be married even if he had to be carried to dear Miss Robin-Red-Breast that day.

But it was no use he could not get married he had measles red spotted measles and he could not get married that day.

So Valentine's Day was yesterday and they were not married that day and perhaps Miss Robin-Red-Breast would fly away if they could not get married soon some way, might fly far far far away.

So what could poor Bobolink do, it was true what could poor Bobolink do, the measles looked as if they had come to stay and Miss Robin-Red-Breast might fly far far far away if they did not get married some way.

So Bobolink thought and thought and then he thought perhaps measles have a birthday, if they have a birthday then they would have to go away that day to celebrate their birthday, sure enough they would have to go away for that day.

But how could Bobolink make the measles say they had a birthday and on what day.

Bobolink thought and thought but he could think of no way. Of course if he asked the measles if they had a birthday of course they would say what is a birthday, we never heard of a birthday, naturally measles never did pay any attention to anybody's birthday, it was their way.

And then Bobolink thought and he said I will ask not all measles but just one little red one little red spot that little red

spot could not know what is what just that one little red spot,
I'll find it all alone and I'll make a moan and ask it to tell and
perhaps if I ask it very well the little red spot which looks like
a dot, I'll tell it what will I tell I'll tell it that if it does not tell
it will get shot.

Well he did ask Bobolink did ask the little red spot, the
little red measle spot when measles have a birthday, and he said
if the little red spot would not not tell when the measles had
their birthday, well that little red spot would get shot. So it did
tell, it could not very well not tell, and it told that the measles'
birthday was the very next day.

So then Bobolink knew that just that day all the measles
would be away celebrating their birthday and so quickly he
sent his mother to tell Miss Robin-Red-Breast to get dressed and
come the next day, and they were married that day and they
lived happily ever after and they never ever saw any measles
again.

Rachel was another story, she just lived for glory, she said
I was born to glory, and they said what is glory and she said
look at me and they did and what did they see they thought
they saw Rachel but did they. They did not, what, no they did
not, because Rachel was not there, she was gone to glory, so
they said, where is she gone and she said with scorn do you not
know where I am gone I am gone to glory. This is the story.
Rachel was born that did her no harm, she had a birthday that
did not take her away, she had another birthday and she found
a thorn and the thorn said it was born that day, and Rachel
did say no nobody was born today, I was born today and nobody else has today for their birthday. The thorn was torn when
Rachel threw it away and the thorn did say it is my birthday
and Rachel did say the glory of this day is that it is my birthday.
This led to everything and Rachel was no more and the thorn
was on the floor and Rachel was gone, she was gone to glory and
that is all there is to her story.

Now it is easy to remember that S comes after R, very easy
to remember very very easy to remember very very very easy
to remember that S comes after R. Nobody would think that
R comes after S that would be a mess, so S comes after R but

they stick close together like tar, they are filled with tenderness oh yes, R and S.

Really my wife says S. For all my life says R. Really begins with R and S begins with S, yes yes.

And T comes after S and can anybody guess oh yes oh yes oh yes how completely yes T comes after S. Believe it or not it is true if not new, true.

And now for S.

Sammy and Sally and Save and Susy.

Sammy had his aunt and his aunt had Sammy and his aunt's name was Fanny and Fanny had Sammy.

Sammy was his name and he was funny and he had an aunt Fanny and she was funny.

Sammy could not eat bread or potatoes or chocolate or cake or eggs or butter or even a date, if he did he fainted away, that was his way, a very funny way but it was Sammy's way. His aunt Fanny was not funny that way, but she was funny in another way, whenever she saw a cat or dog a turtle or a bird or a third, a third of anything she had to turn away. She was funny that way.

But Sammy had his aunt Fanny and Aunt Fanny had her Sammy.

Poor dear Sammy.

Now what could he eat, what could be a treat, poor dear Sammy.

A lemonade perhaps or a beefsteak, or a plate or a but dear me no not ice cream, he could not eat cream, nor a birthday cake, he could eat the candles but not the cake, poor dear Sammy.

Sample and example.

His Aunt Fanny did not care that Sammy could not share what she ate, she just went on cooking and eating and Sammy just went on looking and fainting. They were very funny Sammy and his Aunt Fanny. Poor dear Sammy.

And in spite of all Sammy grew tall tall enough to go to school.

In school they were taught

Sample and Example.

There was a pretty girl and she had a curl and her name was Sally. They called her pretty Sally and she was a sample. And then there was Sammy there just was Sammy poor dear Sammy and he was an example.

And then one day pretty Sally in play asked Sammy to come to her house on her birthday.

Sammy did.

There was a great big cake with frosting and a date and Sammy feeling faint said he could not eat icing or the date or cake but he could eat candles if they were to be given. But no said Sally oh no don't you know, we burn them, there are no candles when we come to eating we burn them and if we did not burn them I would not have my next one not my next birthday, oh naughty Sammy wants to take my next birthday away.

And poor Sammy had nothing to say, to see all that icing and cake made him feel faint so he just did have to go away.

Now you may think this is a funny story but no it is true, anybody even you could know Sammy poor dear Sammy and his Aunt Fanny, he lives there too and it is true all the story of Sammy all the story of his Aunt Fanny all the story of Aunt Fanny all the story of Sammy is true. Poor dear Sammy.

Save and Susie were twins.

And when that begins

They just go on being twins.

Saturday is an awful day they used to say but you would not expect that twins would object to Saturday.

But they did.

They just did object to Saturday.

Now what could be a reason for this.

Saturday ought to be full of bliss.

But there is nothing to say they did object to Saturday.

And the reason for it was this.

Twins can have cousins of course,

And cousins can make twins cross,

And these twins they had cousins,

And you could never guess

But the cousins of these twins,

Were triplets, no less.

And they did come every Saturday
To stay all day with the twins,
And that made the twins very cross,
Because instead of two and two being four and no more,
It was two and three which was very nasty,
Because it was it all ways was three and two and nobody
could like that not they or you not at all. And so it was two and
three which makes five and that was not all.

The triplets had cousins too and what do you think these
cousins were they were quadruplets much more yet than triplets
or twins, oh so much more and when it begins oh so much more,
and these quadruplets came to play every Saturday with the
triplets and twins and every Saturday was a worse day so you
see why the twins were cross of course.

And then what did the quadruplets have they had cousins
too and these cousins were quintuplets, just think of that and
they came every Saturday to play so it made the twins just two,
and the triplets just three, and the quadruplets four and no more
and the quintuplets five and every one of them alive.

It was more than the twins could endure and they hated
Saturday more and more, and they used to roll on the floor to
say how they hated Saturday more and more.

And this was not all.

The twins had their birthday on the same day being twins
that was of course and that did not make them cross, but when
they had their birthday the triplets and the quadruplets and the
quintuplets came to stay and eat all the birthday cake away,
why not, when they were only twins and the others were triplets
and quadruplets and quintuplets what could twins do against
that, they might just as well have been one cat,

Oh dear.

And then the triplets had their birthday of course all three
on the same day and the twins went there but naturally they did
not care to because they were only twins and there were the
triplets well the triplets did not care for it either, they were
better than twins they were three against two it was true when
it came to eat their birthday cake but what were three when the

quadruplets and quintuplets were there who did not care about triplets and twins not at all.

And then the quadruplets had their birthday they of course were all four born on the same day and the twins and the triplets came too to say how do you do but the four and the quintuplets were there well naturally triplets and twins did not get their share.

And the quintuplets had their birthday and that was more still because there were five all born the same day and all eating their cake away, the quadruplets and the triplets and the twins naturally had no share, the quintuplets were there.

So you can see what the twins felt about Saturday, it was all right to be twins but other things Save and Susie said it was too much they hated it to be such, such a way to be, to be nothing but twins and have cousins who were triplets whose cousins were quadruplets whose cousins were quintuplets, it certainly was too much, and Save and Susie the twins rolled on the floor to say they would not stand it any more.

But there was nothing to do every Saturday was there and every birthday too and there was nothing to do for the twins but to boohoo which they did every day before and after when they would all get together and they were only twins only only twins each one only a twin and so they never could win when there were cousins of triplets, quadruplets and quintuplets, no no no, it is even so.

The moral of which is do not only be twins but if you are twins do not have cousins and if you have cousins do not have them be triplets and quadruplets and quintuplets. No no no, it should not be arranged so, but Save and Susie could not change, if you are twins and that begins you just go on being twins.

And now there is T.

Thornie and Tillie and Tender and True.

And after T well there are a lot of useless letters, just think of them all U V W X Y Z, just think of them all there they are pushed up at the end just like a ball, and there is nothing to do at all not with them all but just the same they each have a name so useless they are but they cannot be put into a jar and they cannot be covered with tar they must be just made to go just as if it was not so that there was no use in their being there just to stare.

But first comes T and that is like you or me a very necessary T.

Thornie and Tillie and Tender and True.

Thornie Rose and Tillie Brown had never lived in a town.

Thornie's mother was a missionary in China.

Tillie's father was a missionary in China.

Thornie swam in the river with little Chinese boys.

Tillie sang songs with little Chinese girls.

And then one day Tillie saw Thornie and Thornie saw Tillie.

There were so many little Chinese boys and little Chinese girls around that you could hardly see the ground but Thornie saw Tillie and Tillie saw Thornie, and they were both there.

So Thornie said he would not swim he said he would talk to Tillie and all the Chinese boys said that was silly, but all the same Tillie and Thornie began and Tillie was to sing but when she saw Thornie she did not sing, she did not even begin but she said she would talk to Thornie and the little Chinese girls all said to Tillie but that is silly, but Thornie and Tillie did not think it was silly and that is what they did say. Thornie and Tillie.

Thornie Rose and his mother Mrs. Rose and Tillie Brown and her father Mr. Brown were standing and around them were miles and miles of them Chinamen and Chinese women and Chinese children, miles and miles and miles of them and they were all singing.

Tender and true and all for you.

And as they were singing Tender and True and all for you there were more and more of them Chinese men and Chinese women and Chinese children and there were more and more miles of them more miles of Chinese men and Chinese women and Chinese children they were singing Tender and True and all for you and then Thornie Rose and Mrs. Rose and Tillie Brown and Mr. Brown began singing too, Tender and True and all for you and all of them the miles and miles and more miles and miles of Chinese men and Chinese women and Chinese children and Thornie Rose and Mrs. Rose and Tillie Brown and Mr. Brown were singing Tender and True and all for you and they went on singing all of them went on singing and then it was morning and they all went on singing, singing and singing Tender and True and all for you and then it was evening.

And then they decided to go to bed but how could they go to bed when there were not any beds to go to bed in and so as there were no beds to go to bed in they went on singing Tender and True and all for you.

And then everybody sat down all the miles and miles and more miles and miles of Chinese men and Chinese women and Chinese children and Thornie Rose and Mrs. Rose and Tillie Brown and Mr. Brown. And when they were all sat down they all began to frown.

Then they all said this will not do it will not do for us all to sit down and frown no it will not do, so they all said all the miles and miles and more and more miles of Chinese men and Chinese women and Chinese children and Thornie Rose and Mrs. Rose and Tillie Brown and Mr. Brown, they all said what shall we do since it will not do to just sit down and frown.

So they decided that each one should tell something, they should tell about the day they were born, but said the miles and miles and more and more miles of Chinese men and Chinese women and Chinese children and Thornie Rose and Mrs. Rose and Tillie Brown and Mr. Brown we do not remember when we were born.

And they all once more began to sit down and frown.

This will never do we must do something they all said we might just as well be dead if we were never born.

Of course we were born said all the miles and miles of Chinamen and Chinese women and Chinese children and more and more miles of them and Thornie Rose and Mrs. Rose and Tillie Brown and Mr. Brown, of course we were born. Well perhaps if we keep on remembering we can remember being born. Well they went on remembering all of them but they could not remember the day they were born they remembered the first birthday but they could not remember the day they were born and then the miles and miles of Chinamen and Chinese women and Chinese children and the more and more miles of them and Thornie Rose and Mrs. Rose and Tillie Brown and Mr. Brown they wondered if it would do them any harm if they could not remember the day they were born.

They all had something to say about the day they were born and every birthday they had had since the day they were born and they went on to say everything they had to say each one of them was saying everything they had to say about the day they were born and every birthday they had had since that day and as they were all telling it all of them the miles and miles of Chinese men and Chinese women and Chinese children and the more and more miles of Chinese men and Chinese women and Chinese children and Thornie Rose and Mrs. Rose and Tillie Brown and Mr. Brown the night passed away and they all had forgotten to frown and so then it was the next day and as soon as it was the next day they all began to sing Tender and True and all for you, and so everything was gay and everybody had had something to say and now everybody had something to sing Tender and True and all for you and that was the end of everything, and they all lived happily along and they never forgot their song Tender and True and all for you not any of them not the miles and miles of Chinamen and Chinese women and Chinese children and more and more and more miles of Chinese men and Chinese women and Chinese children and Thornie Rose and Mrs. Rose and Tillie Brown and Mr. Brown.

This all sounds funny but give them money and it is not funny.

Oh yes oh no of course.

This is of course

If no one is ever cross,

Of course of course.

And then you can sing Tender and True and all for you and this is that thing.

The end of the beginning.

The beginning of the ending.

Of course.

As I said T is the last letter that is not funny after that all the letters are as funny as money of course they are.

There is U.

U. Uno, Una, Ursula and United.

Uno and Una.

Uno knew Una and Una knew Uno.

You know that.

Uno was a boy and Una was a girl and Uno's eyes were blue and Una's eyes were brown, and Una's eyes were blue and Uno's eyes were brown. You know that.

Well perhaps it was not just like that. Uno was a boy. You know that, and Uno had one eye that was blue and one eye that was brown and this sounds as if it were not true but it is true you know that. And Una was a girl and she had two eyes too and one eye was blue and one of her eyes was brown. You know that, so Uno and Una one was a boy and one was a girl but each one had one blue eye and each one had one brown eye, and it sounds as if it were not true but it was true you know that.

Uno's right eye was blue and his left eye was brown and Una's left eye was blue and her right eye was brown.

Uno and Una they could both look up and down. But you know that.

What happened when each one had one eye which was brown and one eye which was blue. What did happen.

They were Uno and Una and what did happen.

Well you know what did happen.

Uno's mother had an eye which was blue and an eye which was brown but not Uno's father he had two eyes just the same there were two and they were both blue.

Una's father had an eye which was blue and an eye which was brown but not Una's mother. She had two eyes which were the same both eyes were brown.

But you can see that Uno having a mother with one eye brown and one eye blue and Una having a father like that too one eye brown and one eye blue, it was natural for Uno and for Una when they looked at each other to look with one eye brown and one eye blue and to see another with one eye brown and one eye blue too.

So there they were and naturally well it was natural enough they were married one to the other and they had quite a lot of little children and every single one of all of them had one eye brown and one eye blue.

Well that was the way they were born and of course it did make a good deal of a bother, not when they were all there together it was a rather nice mixture of brown and blue and when they looked at you it was kind of funny nobody exactly knew which was who and beside that if they opened one eye and closed one eye well how would you know whether their eyes were brown and blue. It was a good deal of a bother, not to a sister or to a brother because they were all alike and it just made them bright to have two eyes different one from the other but to any one else it was a good deal of a bother.

And then there was the question of clothes and birthdays. You always match the eyes in little girls' clothes and little boys' shirts and ties, and what could you do if one eye is brown and one eye is blue just what could one do, how could they match the color.

And then there was the birthday cake when each one had a birthday to celebrate, the candles on the birthday cake should match the color of the eyes everybody knows that is wise and what color could the candles be that lit the birthday cake of any of the three, just what color could it be, oh dear, it was a difficult thing to decide and then the one whose birthday cake it was and who had it to cut if he shut the brown eye the brown candles looked shy and if he shut the blue eye the blue candles would try to look away. It was not a natural thing to have two colors of candles and icing on a birthday cake but oh my however you try what could you do if you wanted to match the color of the eye.

Because you know however you try when you cut a birthday cake you always shut one eye. Oh my it was a bother and they could never decide what to do brown or blue.

And then one day there was a war and papa Uno went away to the war. You know he went away. And when he was away oh dear they shot one eye away, it was the blue eye and they made a glass eye and when he came back from the war he did not any more have one brown eye and one blue, but the two, both his eyes were brown and not blue.

This frightened them all and they began to fall on the floor and cover their eyes and cry. And they cried and they cried and they tried not to cry but it frightened them so to see his two eyes brown and not one brown and one blue that they just cried and cried and cried and cried. And they stopped crying and looked up with their eyes all swollen with crying they almost commenced again because it was true each one had been crying so that now no, their two eyes were not one brown and one blue but they were all blue all their eyes were blue all through. It sounds funny but it is true. And so there was no one of them except the mother Una who had one eye brown and one eye blue and it is funny but it is true.

And after that when each one of the children had their clothes and their ties they could match their eyes and when they had their birthday cake, the cake and the icing could be all blue and if they closed one eye to cut their cake there was no mistake because either eye was blue.

This is all true.

Ursula and United.

Well Ursula said United.

And they said what.

And she said United States.

And they said what.

And she said United States of America.

That was because Ursula was tall and that was not all, Ursula was tall and she was born in a state of the United States of America.

Was she born in a state.

Well let us not state what state.

Because Ursula did not know.

She just did not know.

She did not know in which state of the United States of America she was born she just did not know.

Nobody told her so but she just did not know.

Very well she just did not know.

She liked to count it was Ursula's way so she counted the letters in the alphabet and she counted the letters in the word birthday but she did not like to count the number of states in the United States of America because if she should make a mistake she might you know, she was almost always right when she counted but she might make a mistake and if she did make a mistake and she did not count right she might leave out in her count the state in which she was born and if she left out that state and she did not know which state it was anyway well then she could never have a birthday if that state had been left out and she began to pout and went away. So it was not easy for Ursula to say why she would not count the states in the United States when she loved to count and she counted everything else in every way.

But there it was it was because she did not know in which state of the United States she was born and she could never say.

And there she was one day and she was in a desperate way and she just felt she had to do it today, she just did have to count the states in the United States today.

So she began.

How many states were there anyway and why could not she say in what state she was born just why could not she say.

Well it was a funny reason it was a season when there was a storm when she was born and they were riding along that is her mother and her father were riding along in a boat on a river and they were coming under a bridge and there was a storm and suddenly there was a storm and suddenly Ursula was born and nobody could say in which state they were anyway, four states came together just that way and where was Ursula born, poor dear Ursula she used to say when they asked her in school where she was born she used to say I cannot say and then they all though it was a funny way to be born and it was.

She knew she had a birthday that was all she could say and she got sadder and sadder and she wanted to be gladder and gladder so one day she ran away, she ran away and she found a boat and she took it away and she went looking around on the water every way to find the place she was born so she could say I was born in a state as well as on a day, and she asked her way and she asked every way and she could not find out and at last she saw a man who was stout sitting in a boat and she commenced to tell him what it was all about. Oh sure he said I remember that storm I remember that day the day you were born and I can say you bet I can say just exactly the day just exactly the storm just exactly the way just exactly the place you were born. Sure I can, come away come away and I'll show you the way.

And he did and there it was the place where she was born and she said in a great state is it a state or is it not a state this spot where I was born.

Of course it's a state said the man who was stout and who had pointed it out of course it's a state it is the state of Illinois.

Oh said Ursula oh it is the state of Illinois oh joy oh joy I was born in Illinois oh joy oh joy.

And there it was and she could go home and when they said to her in what state were you born she could say Illinois oh joy oh joy and she would never go away she would never stay away from the state where she was born because it made her nervous to think it might shrink or might go away oh no she would always stay and have a birthday in the state in which she was born.

And now she could count the states of the United States every day and when she came to Illinois she would say oh joy oh joy because Illinois was the state in which she was born and in which every year she had her birthday and so she did not get sadder and sadder but gladder and gladder.

And this is the story of Ursula and United and the end of the U's.

V is Van Virgil Valeska and Very.

Van can a man.

What will Van do.

What will he do.

He do.

Van can a man.

Van was his name but all the same he had another name. His name was Papa Woojums spelled like this and when he said it he meant it. Fortunately not.

What.

Not.

Forget me not.

That is Papa Woojums' name.

No one was to blame.

What
Not.
Forget me not.
Van came.
Van is not the same as a weather vane.

But it is up high all the same, and it is a rooster and it knows why, and knows how to tell the wet from the dry. Oh my.

To come back to Van who has a name the same name all the same.

Please be very careful of it.
If you have a name please be very careful of it.
If your name is Papa Woojums
Please be very careful of it.
This is what happened to it.
Not to Van not to Papa Woojums but to the name.
The name Papa Woojums' name was forget me not.
What What he said.
And the name said.
What what forget me not.
How likely to be in a knot.
Dear forget me not.
And anxious to oblige.
Well this is what happened to the name.

There was Papa Woojums and Mama Woojums and Baby Woojums.

And Papa Woojums said what what, and Mama Woojums said Not Not and Baby Woojums said forget me not.

After that there was no secrecy, Van was his name and he was a man and they called him Papa Woojums, just please just think of that.

And then there was a hill and its name was Virgil.

By that time there was a ham and they called it lamb. Well that was a mistake of course. Lamb is a ram or a sheep or mutton it is not a ham.

But Van well he would not make such a mistake and Virgil is a hill and a hill would not make such a mistake not until he did make such a mistake. It would be lighter to make such a mistake than heavier.

Van then, he is a man.

Virgil till, he is a hill.

No mistake at all about that.

Now what happened

What did happen.

Certainly something did.

By mistake.

And a mistake is mistaken.

Oh yes.

What happened.

It is all very confused but more confused than confusing.

Papa Woojums took a picture of a hill which he will, Virgil.

And on the hill grew forget-me-nots.

Papa Woojums began to cry as he began to try to say forget-me-nots.

Very likely forget-me-nots.

How could a birthday come out of forget-me-nots.

Then there suddenly was a story.

When Van that is Papa Woojums was a little boy.

He was not like other little boys.

He had big teeth that bit.

And he wrote poetry.

When his big teeth bit he wrote a poem and when he wrote a poem his big teeth bit.

He was that kind of a little boy.

He wrote a poem about forget-me-nots.

And as he wrote a poem about forget-me-nots his big teeth bit.

Oh not he wrote oh not a forget-me-not.

If you forget me what will I do I will bite with my big teeth all the way through to you.

And he went on writing a poem.

I am Papa Woojums and I'll climb a hill.

Virgil Virgil Virgil.

And he went on writing a poem.

I have a hill, Virgil, I have forget-me-nots when I will, and I was born not on a hill, no Virgil not a hill I was not born on a hill I was born with teeth that bite tight, on a bed of forget-me-nots which were a delight. I am Papa Woojums I am Van and when I bite well when I do nobody ran they just stood too and said boohoo, look at the forget-me-nots too.

Well it happened just like this.

Anybody who writes poems, do they,

Do they have teeth that bite with all their might.

Do they have hills Virgils,

Do they have forget-me-nots,

Plots forget-me-nots,

Or do they have butter-cups.

It is easy to sigh when you say butter-cups.

It is easy to say oh my when you say butter-cups.

But that is not a poem.

A poem has to have big teeth,

And a poem has to say forget-me-nots.

I do not know why

But this is no lie.

That is what a poem has to do.

And a poem has to have a birthday. How could one know how old a poem is if it never had a birthday.

Van Papa Woojums was always sure that it would be a cure for anybody with measles or mumps to see Papa Woojums bite out a poem with teeth so big and forget-me-nots so blue and who are you and it was true, when anybody had measles or mumps and of course mumps is made of bumps, all Papa Woojums had to do was to bite a poem through through his big teeth and away they would go measles and mumps would go up the hill to Virgil.

All right there is no use saying this is not right. Every poem has a birthday and now everybody knows how, please bow. That is what Van Papa Woojums would say every day. Just like that. A cat, and a birthday and teeth big teeth and a forget-me-not and what.

Well what.

Nothing.

Just nothing at all.

Remember.

Just nothing at all.

How about it.
Remember
Just Nothing at all.
And yet
It is better yet.
That Van Papa Woojums is there with white hair what do
you care,
Well big teeth and forget-me-nots and poems and a birthday.
That is what Van Papa Woojums has to say.
Big teeth and forget-me-nots and poems and a birthday.
Poem. Hoe them, toe them.
On his birthday.
And now Valeska and Very.
Valeska did not know any one.
She said Leave it to me.
But she did not know any one
Not even a little girl.
Very she said Valeska said it is very disagreeable not to
know anybody not even a little girl. Very.
Then Valeska began to move mountains and after she moved
mountains she began to move oceans and after that she said it is
very disagreeable not to know anybody, very disagreeable not
to know anybody not even a little girl.
Very.
Valeska said Very because she liked very she liked very very
much. She was always saying very. That is what made her move
oceans and mountains, so she did say very.
Then she said if an oyster has a pearl why can I not know a
little girl.
Then she said because if I say very, then very easily I will
not be very much nearer what I very often like to have very
nearly better than if it was the very best.
It is so very easy to move oceans and so very easy to move
mountains but it is not very easy it is not very easy at all to know
a little girl.
The more Valeska thought about knowing a little one the
more she was careful to very carefully move oceans and to very
carefully move mountains. Then she thought of moving the bed.

She said if she moved the bed it would make a noise a very little noise but still a noise. So she did not move the bed.

The bed was very nearly ready to be moved but Valeska did not move the bed.

Then when she was left to herself of course she was always just alone because she never knew anybody not even a very little girl.

Still when she was left to herself she moved all the mountains and all the oceans back to where they were, not completely back to where they were, she was a little careless and they did not go quite back to where they were, she did not mix them up, no not that but they did not go back quite to where they were.

She might have been very sorry but was she was she very sorry.

She said Very.

Now if you are all alone and do not even know a very little girl can you have a birthday. How can you have a birthday if there is nobody there to tell you what day you were born nothing but oceans and mountains and they have been moved around.

Valeska was very much alone she did not know anybody not even a very little girl.

Valeska said Very.

Perhaps it was all for the best.

Perhaps.

Perhaps it was best that Valeska should say Very.

Perhaps.

Perhaps yes perhaps no.

Who knows.

Certainly she did say it.

Certainly she said Very.

It is not certain that she did not have a birthday but it is certain that she did not know anybody not even a very little girl. It is also certain that she said Very.

V is V and W is W.

One piece less or one piece more, less makes V and more makes double V or double v let me see, Very well let me see.

Double you. Double you is two for you.

Very was V and double you is a double of you. You and you.

But really not, what what, no really not, it is a trouble to think double and when double you makes double V and when double v makes double you it is better to be v than u and yet u could be v if it was a trouble to you.

Now you see why very is very necessary.

So now there double you which is double v. Like it or not, what.

W is Wendell and Worry and William and Wife.

W is also ewe a ewe lamb.

Yes.

Well there was Wendell.

Wendell was thin very thin, he was as thin as a pin.

Wendell and Worry. It was a worry to Wendell to be so thin, as thin as a pin.

And then little by little he said he would eat a lamb and when he saw the little lamb and the little lamb looked like a little dog and everybody who saw the little lamb said look at the little lamb you would say it was a little dog, well then there was no way for Wendell to eat the little lamb, so Wendell just kept on being thin thin as a pin. It was a worry to him but he was thin oh dear yes he was thin he was as thin as a pin.

Wendell was thin as a pin and he stuck in.

When he stuck in he also stuck out

Which would not have been so if he had been stout.

When he stuck out he stuck himself that is easy to see when a pin sticks in and sticks out anybody can stick themselves on that pin when they are not careful what they are about.

Wendell did worry about being stout, he said if he were stout he would not be thin and if he were not thin he would not be a pin and if he were not a pin he would not stick out and if he did not stick out what would it all be about.

Well what would it all be about.

It is easy to see that Wendell was that way that everything was a worry to him.

Then he began to think about fishes.

You can catch fishes with a bent pin attached to a string and did oh did Wendell think if he bent double like a bent pin and he tied a string to himself did he think then that he could catch fish which was his wish.

Did he.

He worried about that.

There was so much to worry Wendell and he worried about that.

Perhaps he would go on getting thin perhaps he would get thinner than a pin and what is thinner than a pin, nothing, and so if Wendell became thinner than a pin what would he become nothing, nothing.

Anybody can see that that would be a worry to him.

He would look at a pin hole and see if he could steal in and hide himself in a pin hole, why not if he was as thin as a pin but as he was a boy he was larger than a pin so although he could get in he stuck out and if he stuck out what was it all about.

They might step on him thinking he was a pin but such a long pin that they did not know what it was about.

You can easily understand that everything was a worry to him.

And so as he was sticking in and out of his pin hole, he saw William William and his wife as large as life and William saw him, and William said to his wife when he saw Wendell, this should be a lesson to him, it should be a lesson to him not to be as thin as a pin.

That was easy for William, William was stout so there was nothing for William to worry about.

But William was kindly even if he was stout and even if he said to his wife, it should be a lesson to Wendell not to be as thin as a pin, so he decided to help Wendell out of the pin hole which he was in and out of which he was sticking.

So William went to help Wendell out and he caught hold of him to pull him out of the pin hole he was in, and naturally enough when William who was stout took hold of Wendell who was thin as a pin Wendell stuck into him and William let out a shout and he said what is it about and he said Wendell who was as thin as a pin had stuck into him. And William's

wife said let it be a lesson to you William never to catch hold
of any one as thin as a pin.

But since Wendell though he was as thin as a pin was as long
as a boy there was no way for William to go away because Wendell was stuck right through him.

So there they were William was like a butterfly stuck
through with a pin and it did him no good to cry because he
was stuck through the whole of him by Wendell who was as
thin as a pin and Wendell was still in his pin hole and the only
one free was the wife of William and all she could see was that
it should be a lesson to them, just be a lesson to them not to be
so thin not to be so stout not to be so ready to shout not to be
so ready to go about. In short it should be a lesson to them.

So they began to sink down, Wendell like a bent pin and
William on top of him and the wife of William dancing around
them and crying it should be a lesson to them it should be a lesson
to them and Wendell was worrying, because to be a bent pin
was a bad thing but if William was on top of him there would
be nothing left of him not even a pin hole oh dear.

And then it was queer, just opposite where all this was was a
laundry and they were washing clothes and they were hanging
them out with clothespins, and William's wife rushed over
there she took a clothespin and she rushed back to Wendell and
William and she took hold of Wendell with the clothespin and
she pulled him out of the pin hole, now they were out of the
pin hole, but they were still stuck together as Wendell who was
thin as a pin had gone right through William who was stout,
and William's wife said, it should be a lesson to him not to be so
thin, it should be a lesson to him.

Now what should they do.

Well William's wife had an idea, now they were clear of the
pin hole she took the clothespin and she took hold of Wendell
she took hold of him with the clothespin and she pulled him
through William all the way through and now there was nothing to do because Wendell was not in William any more and
William had a hole in him the size of a pin but since William
was stout that did not count. Oh dear no.

So.

Well so well so.

What could they do next.

William's wife said it should be a lesson to them but was it.

So then they thought they would fill up the pin hole in William but with what.

And then just opposite was a window and in the window was a cake and the cake was a birthday cake. William's wife saw it first and she said let us take it away and melt the icing first and pour it into the hole and then melt the candles and then seal up the ends and then nobody will know that William had a pin hole in him.

Well that was the way they saved the day.

Wendell who was thin as a pin made his way in into the window he could just creep in, it worried him lest the window should close on him, because even a pin can be smashed flat and thin, but he got in and then he got out and William who was stout was waiting for him with his pin hole all through him. And then they worked all day and William's wife melted the icing and Wendell who was so thin was worried lest they should spill it so he poured it in, and they melted a candle and filled up one end and they melted the icing and poured it in, and when it was all in, they melted the candles and filled the end in and now nobody could tell by looking at him that William had ever been stuck all through with a pin.

And then well then William said it would be a lesson to them, and still there was that birthday cake and even if they had melted all the icing and candles they might as well eat the cake. That was William. Naturally being stout he knew what he was about when cake was around, and even Wendell who was as thin as a pin he could eat birthday cake even though it did make him ache because he was so thin and that was a worry to him and William's wife ate the cake too, she said it should be a lesson to them to the ones that made the cake not to leave it standing where anybody could get in, beside said William's wife they would have cut it with a knife which would have hurt the birthday cake, but we just first melted everything and we did not hurt anything, and anyway said William it ought to be a lesson to them.

And now X.

X is difficult, and X is not much use and it is kind of foolish that X should have been put into the alphabet, it almost makes it an elephant.

X is Xantippe and Xenophon and Xylophone and Xmas.

Xantippe and grip her and Xenophon.

There is no use in saying that Xenophon did not know Xantippe because he did. How else could they both have commenced with X, how else.

X is funny anybody knows that it is funny even X itself knows it is funny.

Xantippe and Xenophon.

And then perhaps it was the letter X perhaps it was but anyway all of a sudden Xantippe did not seem real to Xenophon and Xenophon did not seem real to Xantippe.

Xantippe and grip her and Xenophon could get no grip on Xantippe and Xantippe could not get any grip on Xenophon.

So what did they do. They thought they would part with the letter X. First Xantippe thought she would and then Xenophon. But if they quit the letter X if they lost it like they might a stick which they threw away after a dog had bitten it in play if they did what would happen then then they would be Antippe and Enophon and somehow they felt then as if nobody would ever any more pay them any attention. They knew then that it was the X and not the then that made everybody pay attention to them.

So they just had to begin again and have X where it had been and they just had to be Xantippe and Xenophon even if Xantippe was not real to Xenophon and Xenophon was not real to Xantippe.

So they started over again, X to X, Xantippe to Xenophon.

And what happened then. Well this happened then, they saw five men and ten women and the ten women and the five men walked behind them walked behind Xantippe and Xenophon.

Xantippe and Xenophon knew they were there but they could not look at them because if they looked at them then the X in Xantippe and the X in Xenophon might frighten the ten women and the five men and if the X's frightened them they might try to kill them. When people are frightened this does happen and Xantippe knew this and so did Xenophon.

What could they do then.

Of course it was all the fault of the X's but they had tried to do without them and that did not suit either of them.

What could they do now, if it were true of you that you were Xantippe or you were Xenophon now what could you do.

Well truly really truly, you could not do anything, you could just wait for something and when something was nothing and nothing was something, then Xantippe and Xenophon were nothing and something.

It was very discouraging and there were the ten women and the five men following, they were always following them.

So then they thought of something, they thought they would change the X in Xantippe for the X in Xenophon, that might help them. So they immediately went to work to exchange them, they changed the X in Xenophon for the X in Xantippe and they did it quickly and completely and then they went on walking, but no the five men and the ten women were still behind them following them, so exchanging one X for the other X had not made it impossible to recognize them not at all, not either one of them not either Xantippe or Xenophon.

So once more that was all and they began to be afraid they would fall and the five men and the ten women would catch them. It was frightening, it did frighten Xantippe and Xenophon.

And if the five men and ten women never went away how could Xantippe and Xenophon stay anywhere that day.

So they thought they would try again to change everything, they thought they would change the birthday of Xenophon for the birthday of Xantippe and that would so change them being born another day would change any one, they thought that this would so change them that no one would know that they were Xenophon and Xantippe Xantippe and Xenophon and the five men and ten women would then go away.

Not at all.

They knew the five men and ten women they knew that Xantippe and Xenophon were Xantippe and Xenophon even if they had changed their birthdays and the five men and ten women kept coming after them and Xantippe and Xenophon did not know what to do and they did not know what to say.

So it happened all of a sudden, the five men and ten women they walked so quickly they walked right into Xenophon and Xantippe and as they walked into them all five of them the men and all ten of them the women opened their mouths as if they were yawning and just then Xenophon and Xantippe disappeared down the mouths of them and no one ever saw Xantippe and Xenophon again and the ten women and five men went away.

And now we have Xylophone and Xmas.

Every one knows what a Xylophone is well does every one. You tap on it and it makes a noise well so does any one.

And X stands for Christmas well any would would any one.

A Xylophone wishes it was the best of all because if it was the best of all it would be given for Christmas. Christmas is so confused, it knows perfectly well perfectly well that there is an X in Christmas and still there it is when there is something to sell there it is there is an X in Christmas.

It is very confusing not at Christmas when there is something to sell but when it is just Christmas that is Christmas.

It is very confusing, why should there be an X in Christmas when there is no X in Christmas why should there be one and why should the Xylophone not be the best of all when when they sell them and they spell them with an X at Christmas.

Life is very confusing said the Xylophone to his Mrs.

Very very confusing said Xmas to Christmas.

There is not much use in a Xylophone being a Xylophone said the Xylophone to his Mrs., not much consolation said the Xylophone not much consolation because the X is not a C no consolation for me said the Xylophone to his Mrs. even if Christmas is Xmas. He can turn a C into an X but a Xylophone a Xylophone can not turn an X into a C.

So why be why be why be.

Why be he, why be a Xylophone.

A Xylophone

Oh dear me.

So the Xylophone made a groan and his Mrs. thought a thought she thought she would give the Xylophone a C for Christmas and so the C would not be only a consolation to a Christmas but it would also be a consolation for the Xylophone.

You see where the C comes in.

It comes in in comes and in consolation.

So the Mrs. of the Xylophone thought Christmas would be an occasion to give a C to the Xylophone.

Now that seemed all right but was it all right.

It was not all right and the reason it was not all right was this.

In the first place nobody wanted a Xylophone for Christmas and if nobody wanted a Xylophone for Christmas how could the Mrs. of the Xylophone afford to give the Xylophone a C for Christmas.

And then the Mrs. of the Xylophone, well she was very tempted she really was she thought well she thought she would steal she just thought she would she just thought she would steal, yes there is no other word to use for it she would just steal the C from Christmas to give it to the Xylophone. After all at Christmas Christmas did not need a C it was always using an X and when the poor Xylophone whom nobody wanted to buy for Christmas wanted the C for a consolation what harm would it do to steal it from Christmas.

Well Christmas did not feel that way about it not at all, it wanted its X and it wanted its C and nobody so Christmas thought nobody nobody could expect it to give or lend or have stolen from it its C. What was it going to do all year with only an X and not a C. Oh dear me. Anybody could see that it was not possible for Christmas to do without both its X and its C oh dear me.

So Christmas sat up and said no when the Mrs. of the Xylophone tried so quietly to come in and steal its C away to give it to the Xylophone who wanted it for consolation. No said Christmas no, no no. I need my X and I need my C go away and do not bother me with the Xylophone, nobody wants a Xylophone nobody nobody, nobody wants a Xylophone so what difference is it if it only has an X and not a C for consolation.

It seemed hard of Christmas but Xmas did write it on a card Christmas does, Xmas always writes everything on a card Christmas always does and Christmas wrote to the Xylophone go away and leave me alone nobody wants a Xylophone.

It was hard nobody wanted a Xylophone and the Xylophone's Mrs. could not find one not a solitary C as consolation for the poor Xylophone.

So they started to go home alone the Xylophone and the Mrs. of the Xylophone and as they were bumping along, well the Xylophone did make a tune, and somebody was following them, and they turned around and when they found it was a little boy following them they turned away.

And then they heard the little boy say I like that Xylophone please play I wish I had a Xylophone for my birthday.

Well said the Mrs. of the Xylophone what will you give if we give you one for your birthday. What do you want said the little boy I have no money with which to pay but I would love to have a Xylophone for my birthday. Oh said the Xylophone what I want is a C I want a C for consolation and to be like Christmas who has a C and an X and is always such a great success.

So the little boy said my name is Charlie King and you can have a C or a K either one or both of them if I can have a Xylophone for my birthday. Not a K said they not a K but a C oh yes a C we will take the C from Charlie and here is the Xylophone for your birthday.

And the little boy handed them the C from Charlie and rushed away with the Xylophone for his birthday to play it all day all the day of his birthday.

And Mr. and Mrs. Xylophone went on their way and they were too happy to play the Xylophone because now they had their consolation, they had an X and they had a C just like Christmas and so even on Christmas they had nothing to say except isn't it a lovely evening.

The end of the X's.

Yvonne and You, Yes and Young.

These are the Y's why not.

What, what not.

Oh my.

There is a difference between the beginning and the end if there is nothing to mend.

That is why the Y is always comfortable enough, comfortable enough.

Yvonne and you.

Yvonne was a girl.

She was the youngest of five, perhaps she was the youngest of six, perhaps she was the youngest of seven.

Anyway she was the youngest yet, perhaps that was the reason her name was Yvonne Yet.

There was another family and their name was not Yet it was Young and the next to the youngest one was named Yes Young. Yes that was his name Yes Young, and he could guess that Yvonne Yet would let him come.

Which he did.

What a pleasant day that was for Yvonne Yet, and Yes Young.

They do have funny names around there.

That is natural enough that they have funny names around there if you do not like Y.

Natural enough if they do not like Y around there and they do not like Y. Why, well they just do not like Y. Not well enough not to be shy when they see any one whose name begins with Y.

So what could they do with these two, Yvonne Yet and Yes Young, they were just too full of Y's to get along with any one living around there.

Anyway Yes Young was a policeman and he was marrying he said he was Yvonne Yet.

Yvonne Yet's father and mother, mother and father were sailors.

Yes Young's father and mother and mother and father were bakers.

Yes Young's father and mother baked for sailors, and Yvonne Yet's father and mother sailed for bakers so it was natural enough for Yvonne Yet and Yes Young to get along, particularly as she had been the youngest and he had been next to the youngest, and so they did get along and they were young and strong and the letter Y had not gotten them yet no not yet, yes not yet, you bet.

So there they were married Yvonne Yet and Yes Young and it did not do anybody any harm. Yes Young was a policeman, even if his father and mother did the baking and Yvonne Yet stayed at home even though her father and mother were sailors and were sailing.

So there they were married and they did not have any trouble with the letter Y yet, yes not yet.

Pretty soon the trouble with the letter Y was going to begin.

They heard some one sing and this is the song he sang.
Imagine he sang imagine if you can
Imagine said he and as he said it he sang imagine if you can
What you could plan
Imagine he sang imagine if you can how much it would cost to get back a letter if it could be lost. Imagine that if you can, and his voice rose higher and higher imagine if you can is what he sang if you began to have a name and not a letter for the same.

Imagine that he said and when he said it he sang imagine that if you can.

Yvonne Yet and Yes Young were there, it was an afternoon and everybody was sitting around in a crowd when suddenly this man began to sing and he sang imagine it if you can.

Yvonne looked at Yes and Yes looked at Yvonne. They remembered they had put the letter Y in an envelope and now where was it. Oh dear they said what a mess. Y is certainly the one not to be taken along and others have two letters one different from the other and a husband and a wife they have a different father and a mother so they cannot not have this bother but we oh dear me, Y Y Y Y oh why are we only Y oh why oh why, and they cried so loud that the man who was singing stopped singing just to hear them say Y oh why oh why oh why only Y.

It is sweet said the man singing it is sweet and it is neat to

have the letters A to Z but not the letter Y. Why not the letter
Y. Oh my.

Well it is a very funny story that, why not the letter Y.

The letter Y you see the letter Y is in an envelope and when
it falls into the fire it burns. Now if a letter burns then it is not
there. Believe it or not it is true.

Now the letter Y was put into an envelope they remembered
that and the envelope was put into the fire, that is what happened
to the letter Y. Of course that is what happened to the letter Y
and that is because it is in cry and in Oh my, that is the reason
why the letter Y was put into an envelope, and into the fire and
the envelope was all burned up and in the ashes there were no
sashes there was nothing at all, the letter Y was gone.

It was a very sad story.

And there were Yvonne Yet and Yes Young and they just
did not know what to say.

Yvonne could not say to Yes what do you think Yes because there was no letter Y and Yes Young could not say to
Yvonne I will take care of you Yvonne because the letter Y was
burned away, away away away.

And the worst of it all was that Yes Young was a policeman,
now a policeman should have seen to it that the letter Y was not
put into the envelope and even if it was put into an envelope it
should not have been put into the fire and if it was put into the
fire the fire should have been put out before the envelope was
burnt up.

Yes Young was a policeman and that is what he should have
done. Yes Young.

Well it was a very sad day.

Those are sad days when a letter the only letter that can
make you know that you are you is burned away. Oh dear a very
sad day.

And what did they say.

Well Yes Young was a policeman and he said it is an awful
thing but I will find a way, and Yvonne Yet looked at him and
said do you think you can do anything, and that I will not have
to go away. Not yet, was all Yes Young could find to say.

But he went away to do something.

The first thing he saw was the dog Never Sleeps and he said
if he never sleeps perhaps he can help me find something that
will take the place of the letter Y's and so he called Never Sleeps
and Never Sleeps and Was Asleep woke up and came with him.
He told them what he wanted and they said well I know what
to do, I know a baby is going to be born and they are going to
call it Yvonne, now it does not make any difference to that baby
if they call it Lucy instead of Yvonne because it is just born.
Now we will call out Lucy Lucy and the baby will cry and
they will all say oh my and perhaps Lucy is a prettier name
than Yvonne and that will be Lucy's birthday and so there will
be an Yvonne for Yvonne Yet and so well she is not a baby but
if it is her birthday perhaps it will be just the same.

Well that was a fine idea and they carried it through and
Never Sleeps and Was Asleep cried Lucy Lucy, Baby Baby,
Baby Lucy, Baby Lucy, and everybody said of course we will
call baby who has just been born we will call her Lucy and not
Yvonne. So with the Y from Yvonne the policeman Yes Young
went home.

Well it was Yvonne Yet's birthday, so whatever you say she
was pleased to have it be that way.

But and she began to cry no matter how I try I can not stay
with Yes Young because his letter Y was all burned away, you
have not found another one she said to Yes Young. Not yet, said
the policeman Yes Young I have only just begun.

So off he went again and he thought that Never Sleeps and
Was Asleep were police dogs, well they were not, they were just
little brown dogs but when a policeman called them they did
come.

So they said they would find Yes or Young.

But there were none.

All the Young wanted Young and all the Yes wanted Yes.

So what could a policeman do, Not yet said the policeman
but that was all he could do.

And then one day there on the door he saw a sign which
said Yes Young. It was an empty house it was to let and he said
how could that say Yes Young. Well it was this way. One day,
girls and boys were at play, and one of them did say let's play

that we are younger every day. And they did they began to play that they were younger every day and one of them had written this up on the door while he was lying on the floor he had written on the door Yes Young.

And Yes Young being a policeman he could go in, and he could take the door down and carry it home to Yvonne and then they were just all right again, Yvonne had had her birthday present of Yvonne and Yes Young a policeman had carried away a Yes Young. And so they were very careful after that of the Y's, they never said Oh my and they never said cry and they never said try, they just went on being Yvonne and Yes Young, and they never said Not yet, never, never never. And so they lived happily ever after and had a great many children but they never gave them any name that began with Y not one.

And now it is Z.

Z is not the last but one it is the last one.

Zebra and Zed, Zoology and Zero.

Z is a nice letter, I am glad it is not Y, I do not care for Y, why, well that is the reason why, I do not care for Y, but Z is a nice letter.

I like Z because it is not real it just is not real and so it is a nice letter nice to you and nice to me, you will see.

Zebra and Zed.

A Zebra is a nice animal, it thinks it is a wild animal but it is not it goes at a gentle trot. It has black and white stripes and it is always fat. There never was a thin Zebra never, and it is always well as sound as a bell and its name is Zebra.

It is not like a goat, when a goat is thin there is nothing to do for him, nothing nothing, but a Zebra is never thin it is always young and fat, just like that.

Well there was a little French girl named Zed, she said her name was Zed and it was her name and everybody called her by the same. She was a little French girl and she had a father, her father was not fat he was thin, he was an explorer and if you explore and explore you have to be able to go through any door to explore and so you just have to be thin.

But Zed was not so thin she was quite fat and her father the explorer always brought home for her something especial for her birthday that came from far away.

So Zed said, she held her head, that was because she was not thin but fat and she leaned her head her heavy fat head on her father who was thin and she said father what will you bring me for my birthday and he said what shall I bring, and she said I want a Zebra because he is never thin, I want a Zebra for my birthday.

So her father the explorer went away and he did not forget her birthday, and he did not forget her Zebra and it was easy to get a Zebra because they are always young and fat and they think they are wild but they are not. So it was very easy to catch him the Zebra for Zed's birthday, but Zed was to have her birthday far away and how was her father the explorer to get the Zebra there for her on her birthday.

Well there was no boat there, that with any amount of care could get the Zebra there for Zed's birthday she was having her birthday too far away.

And Zed just had to have her Zebra for her birthday she just had to have it on that day there was nothing else to say she just had to have it on that day otherwise she would hold her head all day. Zed was that way.

So her father the explorer looked around and this was what he found an airplane and he thought if it sailed away in a day it would bring the Zebra to Zed for her birthday.

So the first thing to do was to paint the airplane so it looked like a Zebra too, not red and blue but white and black and in stripes to look like a back.

So that is what the father of Zed started to do he painted the airplane until it looked exactly like a Zebra so when the Zebra was asked to come too, he would think it was a Zebra asking him to come which would be fun and he would come with a run.

Which he did.

There he was on the airplane and now the fun had begun, but in a very little while the Zebra would know that the airplane was all alone it and the Zebra and Zebras like a lot of Zebras around to paw the ground and to be Zebras together and to sound like Zebras and not to be alone, if Zebras are alone they make a moan and say they are not Zebras, and if they say they are not Zebras they are not Zebras and so there would be no use in taking a Zebra to Zed for her birthday if when he got there he was not a Zebra at all, that would not do at all not at all.

So Zed's father thought hard and he decided to paint the clouds and the sky like Zebras black and white stripes, so that as the Zebra sailed past he would say yes at last there are nothing but Zebras all around, it is like the ground all covered with Zebras and I am not alone and so I will not groan but be a Zebra and my black and white stripes will last.

So Zed's father went to work he was in an airplane ahead and he painted so fast the sky and the clouds that as the Zebra's plane came sailing along, the Zebra saw nothing but Zebras around, because even the ground Zed's father the explorer had painted black and white in a stripe like the Zebra, so the Zebra sailed along and never knew he was not there where he had been born with nothing but Zebras everywhere and so he came down to be taken there where they were to prepare that he would not groan because he was alone.

Little fat Zed from her feet to her head was a Zebra, and the house and the trees and even the breeze was painted black and white stripes like a Zebra, so the Zebra was happy to stay and it was her birthday and all that day and all every day she and the Zebra passed in play, they were young and they were fat and that was that and her father the explorer went away to explore some more and to begin again on Zed's next birthday.

Zoology.

Zoology oh dear what is Zoology.

Zoology is all about wild animals thin and stout and they do all shout we are Zoology that is what Zoology is about.

Well once upon a time there was a little thing, he was a dog his name was Never Sleeps and he had a brother Was Asleep and they always were together.

A big dog likes to be with a little dog and a little dog likes to be with a big dog.

That is because it is so flattering for the big dog to have the little dog admire him and for the little dog to be allowed to come with a big dog. Boys are like that and girls are like that, they like a little one to say how big they are and they like a big one to say how little they are. Never Sleeps and Was Asleep were not like that, Was Asleep was asleep and Never Sleeps was awake otherwise they were twins.

Now Never Sleeps when he was not asleep and he never was asleep heard a little boy there was a little boy there and there were three little girls that made four and no more, the little boy was reading a book about Zoology, and at first Never Sleeps however he could try did not understand why the little boy was reading a book about Zoology but pretty soon he heard him tell how dogs just little dogs like Never Sleeps, could be dogs that chased and tore that rushed around not on a floor but in the woods and far away and killed everything that was in their way. Most exciting is what Never Sleeps did say, most exciting.

So he tried to wake Was Asleep but there was no use in that, and there was no use in trying to wake the cat so all alone he went away to be the way the dogs had been before they had been a twin like he was with Was Asleep, just a dog to sleep by night and by day.

Zoology was exciting.

Up to then the worst thing Never Sleeps had ever done was to run to bark and to tear the clothes of those he chose as the ones he loved, he tore their clothes when he was afraid they would go away and leave him there to stay and bark and cry away, and he tore their clothes when he wanted them to come away and he tore their clothes when anything frightened him and being a brave dog, Never Sleeps was a brave dog why anything could frighten him, that is what a brave dog is, and that is the reason everybody can love them because anything can frighten them.

So that is what Zoology was it was frightening, it was frightening for the animals being it all the wild animals and all the tame ones because anything could frighten them and it was frightening to anyone reading about them because anybody reading about them would not know that anything could frighten the wild animals and the tame ones that make Zoology but anything can, thunder and lightning and sun and rain and heat and cold and fog and a train, and other animals and men and even children and women, well that is very nice to know it makes everybody feel brave to know that anything can frighten anybody so.

And Never Sleeps was like that, not Was Asleep, because he was asleep and as he was not frightened by being asleep and he always was asleep he was never awake long enough to be frightened or to frighten.

But Never Sleeps was not like that, he liked to think he was stronger than a cat or a bird or the moon or coming too soon.

So then one day after he had heard all that Zoology had to say he went out to frighten something, not to be frightened but to be frightening. So he went along and he saw a door and he had never noticed that door before and it was a little open. So he put his nose in and a paw and the door opened a little more and he went in.

And there in the dark corner sat a hen and beneath her were the eggs she was hatching to give all twelve little chickens their birthday.

Well when Never Sleeps saw her in the dark on the floor he barked as he never had barked before and he put forward a paw and he knew he was frightened and a little frightening, and he was right because the hen although he had given her a fright knew what to do all right, she rushed at him her wings drumming, and fire like lightning shooting out from one eye and then her other eye, and oh my, the door was shut or shutting and what could Never Sleeps do, or the hen too and all the twelve baby chickens waiting for their birthday.

Just then, well just then there was a moo there was a cow too and she did not like what everybody was doing and Never Sleeps was frightened by that and there was a cat and there was a goat and there was a sheep but there was no boat and oh dear there was no coat to hide in. Well anyway some way Never Sleeps never knew how he was out of the door and he said not ever any more would he listen to Zoology, Zoology was too much, he preferred Was Asleep and the boy but Never Sleeps when the boy was asleep took the book of Zoology and tore it in two and chewed it all through, he had had enough of Zoology

enough and some more. And then there in the dark in the corner
on the floor the hen went on as before and the twelve little
chickens they certainly had and they were glad they had, they
had their birthday on that day, and it was peaceful too and the
cow said moo and the goat was there and a chair and a sheep
to keep and a cat so fat and that was that.

And Never Sleeps was far away and he just had nothing to
say that day.

And now it is Zero.

Oh dear oh Zero.

Zero they said and they felt well fed.

Oh hero dear oh Zero.

Oh hear oh dear oh Zero.

So Zero is a hero

And why is Zero a hero.

Because if there was no Zero there would not be ten of them
there would only be one.

If there was no Zero there would not be a hundred of them
there would only be one.

So Zero is a hero.

And if there was no Zero there would not be a thousand of
them there would only be one.

And if there was no Zero there would not be ten thousand
of them there would only be one.

And if there was no Zero there would not be a hundred
thousand of them there would only be one.

So Zero is a hero.

And if Zero was not a hero there would not be a million of
them there would only be one.

And if Zero was not a hero if he was not a real hero there
would not be a billion of them there would only be one one
single one.

And if Zero was not a hero well if Zero was not a hero how
could anything be begun if there was only one one one.

So Zero is a hero and as Zero is a hero there are ten of them
and each one of them has a birthday instead of only one.

It would be sad to be all alone every birthday so that is
what they all say the ten and the hundred and the thousand and

the ten thousand and the hundred thousand and the million and
the billion they say oh Zero dear Zero oh hear oh we say that
thanks to the Zero the hero Zero we all have a birthday.

Hurray.

And so that is all there is to say these days about Alphabets
and Birthdays and their ways.

ALL SUNDAY

(1915)

It was the custom to believe little children dogs foxes and letters. Foxes is a french name for fox. I leave off hating.

We were so careful of the hat. We came to pick it up. This is a dialogue.

What is Sunday.

Every day will be Sunday.

Every day is Sunday.

Today is Sunday.

We went out walking.

We saw to that.

We were taken farther than yesterday.

We had tea.

We always have tea.

She said she would be better pleased if we were alone together. I think so.

I know kinds of faces.

I know by that.

I believe in the twenty-second of May.

This is a description of fatigue.

Fatigue is rendered attentive by disagreeable insight. Have changes. Do so. Be perfectly allowed. Don't digest salmon. Have splendid fish. Be slender and be satisfied with green letters. You may say you have early papers. You may even be delighted. You may hope to have plenty of introductions.

I wish I could describe hands.

I think your first idea was better. There is not enough continuation in hands. They're too different. It's too shocking.

I say a great deal that isn't so beautiful that you don't put in.

Would you like to put in I mean California. Yes I do.

Do you think I'm California.

I must clean that, it's got dirty, don't suck it.

I am going to do what I'm told.
Let me say that.

HANDSOME SUNDAY.

Hands have been mentioned. One two one two one two one
two one two one two one two one two I am surprised.

PEBICO.

Hands are often when they are cited kept blissful by remem-
brances. Large words, lots of words, have been made by war.
Chiefly mentioned in lists and by all men. All men are brave
and silent. All men are delighted to be separated. All men are
behind what is commonly called duck ribbon. I do not mean
that they do not vanquish. They do. They vanquish excellent
pleasures. For example. Once there was a pleasant Cook. He had
troubles and he showed what he meant when he said that he
was pledged to be tall. He wasn't by birth. He had little rhymes.
Since then he has spread. He has had use for everything. He
has put white on his shoes. He has answered me. We did trust
him. Belonging to thee.
    Are you having a happy Sunday. Yes. Just why it's Sunday
I do not know but we'll let it go.
    I say let us have hands. I specially mean it. I have plenty of
wishes.
    By that time all sound was loud it made a distance. Why
wash birds. They cough.
    Hands. Pretty hands.
    I don't believe in it. I have a perfume. I wish I knew South
America.
    All Sunday I was equal.
    I have instances of this.
    They waited for the boat.
    It was not crowded because two of them were happy.
Modestly so.

I have faith in it.
I have faith in him.
He keeps me by his word.
Press it.
Not fur to me.
Where was he.
Where was he where was he.
By that time it was warm weather.
Public pains.
Character.
Character is the thing that makes forcing exacting. She said she would swim. She said it made her supple.
Why do you not credit it.
Because she does not know the names of fishes.
This is a story.
Once and often we had tea. I know the color. I was right about it. We went every second day every day. It was better. I didn't say I wished it. It was a circumstance and we were not blue-eyed prominent.
Prominent.
I like that name.
The story is Mrs.
Mrs. misses kisses.
Mrs. kisses most.
Second.
Timely.
The story made a special appeal. It was too lucky. How could seldom appear.
By that time fishes were splendid. Pablo was his name. I don't mean it was an accident. He wanted to see McKinley's ring he wanted to be able to say that it was an eagle. It was an eagle, it was a church.
Once Napoleon was down here. He went in at the door. He saw the door slant. He said he would be spared. They say that there is no valor in a rich man. I could say another word. Who wishes it. Not that. He told us, the young man told us that he understood from the words that there was that there were frightful messages. He was not slim. The valet might have been

an intense person. He offered to take a boat and go and relieve us and we said no. Do not do so. Go and see if you can find them. He found one who turned into that thing. She was lovely and searching. She looked about.

I wish to be real.

I am coming to tell one thing. Believe it and say that you are deceived. He said I am.

It's warm.

That's all.

CHAPTER III.

I like a life of adventure. I like passing the night reading poetry. I like measuring pieces of oil paper and filling bottles with oil and drinking whatever I can. I like to sit still and repeat that I am very well and not confused. I like speeches. I even like to select seats. I do wish I was not equal to it.

Later on I find I found out that he was born on that day. It was so certain. It did him mischief. I planned to read. I cannot expect puppies to go under cover and not suffer. I cannot expect to be a mother. Why not. Because there is one. Hurrah.

Plenty of that day.

Words of kindness.

He was nettled by what he said.

Roosevelt wishes us not to travel on Sunday.

I will not add another chapter I will go on.

Why did she stay in that country which is accursed. Why did she say she sympathized with them. Why did she learn to substitute truth and right dealing for falsehood and declaration. Why did she not choose leather. I do not know.

I couldn't I have tried hard but I couldn't.

When I have made up my mind to do a thing I mustn't insist on the weather I must just be ready to look. I do see the wind I do see that the wind is bright. Military delight.

I have always had the belief about Sunday. I don't mean that. I don't mean that I have not known when it was a disappointment. I have known that.

He asked us, could we read. He said he had seen rain in the Pyrenees. I misunderstood Pyramids. He had said Pyramids. He was apt to begin then and he was unlikely to be disappointed. He offered us the use of his valet. His valet was german. I do not mean by his way of thinking, I mean only to repeat that he spoke in English and not harshly. He offered to awake the man who was elderly and slept by the door. Not beside the door but near the gate. We were thankful. We said, thanks so much.

We could not determine why he bowed. He must have been accustomed to that musing. He must undoubtedly read Seneca in Spanish. He must surely have suspicions. He suspects nothing. There is nothing to question. The boat is American. It has a captain. We met three of them. We knew they were deceiving in the same fashion all who had any appointment. We mentioned it to the consul. He said he had been a witness. This does not make hands necessary. I wish I could tell about girls.

There was a whole street where they sold buttons, Mallorcan buttons. They were exactly there.

I am trying to tell a story of the call we made on our friends who always offer us tea. We drink the tea.

Change. The change between summer and winter, between sun and fog, between a man cooking for men and being accustomed to feed them and being tall and not at all quick is marked.

If a cook is fishing is he feeding for cooking. If a cook is cooking is he feeding with the same persuasion. Is he cooking.

A cook is cooking.

A cook is fishing.

It is a joke.

The success of it was that I met him and he said something. He said his mother was earnestly reading.

They asked us to eat something. I said why should we. They said that that was a fair question.

How can I admire beautiful scenery and greens and the smell of satin and see humming bees. I can do all that by traveling and resting. Believe me. I do believe it. There is no use he wouldn't do it.

III.

Seven years a chamber-maid.

We once said that there was to be a rain of stars.

We went out to see it. It was clouded. The clouds were over the moon.

By exchanging courtesies, by bowing by being impressive, by impressing and then there is education. Education makes the most of us.

I wish to describe one day.

They are growing fatter.

Black curses, he despises red faces. Red faces are clean. They are cleaned and washed. Chocolate is a color and a pretty word. So are fire-arms.

No I can't get to do it.

A bottle. A bottle is famous because it has print on it. We exchange books with pleasure.

I love a whole sentence.

I do not despise girls.

I wish to be welcome.

I am very pleased with my account. With my account of it all.

As agreeable as any one.

My accent.

I can hear ship's bells.

Why do you beat Sunday.

In imitating a voice I hear it. I do not see why I mustn't. It pleases me it is ordinarily satisfying and I do not like to climb hills. I mean I do.

The question of languages. The question of languages is interesting. Let us take Mallorcan. They make sounds in speaking. So do Englishwomen. More than that is thrilling.

Take any language. What would be the use of questioning about any such thing. Why is doleful and denying the same thing in speaking. I come to hear a voice.

Hands all hands are selfish. All suppers are felt to be clean. We were spoiled by excess.

Jenny or chicken.

I don't see the necessity, I see the desirability, I see the adaptability and I also see it as reasonable.

Why should any one frighten me.

Go to bed pleasantly.

Go to bed.

Pleasantly.

I heard them say yes.

I am very indifferent to shoes.

The dears.

I am not plastic.

By nearly.

All the time.

Spread out water.

Do spread out rapidly.

This is the story.

We came to see what it was that was wanted. It was not tea. We had that every day. It was not meat. We had that Sunday. It was chicken. We have that every day. It was olives. We had that. It was very good cake.

They bake very well here.

We are sorry to miss coffee. You can eat coffee with bread. Of course you can. It ought to be encouraged. The mistake was made when it was expected that early oranges are not good. They are good. They are very good. The whole plant is good. I come to believe in my choosing. I can easily find those that are not juicy. That is I could. Actually it is not easy to make that mistake because, especially if I cut open a great many, all of them are good and we are satisfied.

We are satisfied on the whole. We do not ask for renown. Yes we do miss.

Let us see the oil.

Let us whistle shrilly.

Lettuce.

That is the word when I laugh. Happily peas are sweet peas

and tender and though we have them we plan to not to save them. Not at all necessarily.

Do be copied by me.

I was so astonished.

When it has rained for some days and we are contented with gloves and deny it why are we so careful of pronunciation. Countess Karoly's curse. We have not that sentence. We have not that hymn. We understand that it is natural to ask did we water the flowers.

Suddenly we find that the letters are stopped. This means that the hotel waiter is not honest. We hope for it. We are sure to find a pleasant way.

A man likes his way he likes to go walking. We hope not to be satisfying. We intend to do as we please. It pleases us to withdraw. We make an excuse of the way. I don't understand it. I mean to be just. I know. I like two thirds. I am easily left with more. I can feel anything. This is not perfectly satisfying but if it isn't one way it's another. This is no time to flatter in which to flatter.

It's disgusting.

Really have I gone so far.

This is the story of how we went walking.

Why should unusual acts remind one of the sea-shore. Why should questions stir the imagination. Why should pins be needed and why should shirts discolor. Why should the walking remain the Mediterranean why should we all be foolish.

The story of it is as follows.

It is easy to be regular and married. It is even necessary.

It is unaccountable to be reserved. It is a solace to fry fish. Fish is the cheapest article of food in those places in which salted fish can be bought when fresh fish has not been received. It is incessant but not a bit tiring.

This is the conversation.

I cannot repeat it.

Do be kind.

I do not wish to remind them of the need of large particles.

Do you remember it was the fifth of September we heard of asphyxiating gases. Do you remember that we could not tell

Emmeline. Do you remember that on the same day we heard that permission had been withheld. Do you remember that we couldn't know how many h's there were in withheld. It all comes back to me how, the war and everything.

I do not like two bottles. I do not like to look at them. They are differently filled. They are filled with the same water. They have not been emptied. They have been opened. They have not been used up together. I will do so.

The story that was told was the obligingness of walking. Are we obliged to go walking. Are we obliged to choose that form of exercise. Are we obliged to decide what we will not do and are we obliged to be pleasant and are we obliged to be present. We are obliged to be present.

We will still read.

IV.

Sunday.
All Sunday.
All Sunday it was raining.
I am that.
This is in consequence.
The consequence is do you demand lilacs, wild flowers or dogs. Do you demand tube roses. Do you like to consider moonlight as natural. Do you believe readily.

There are five germans in Barcelona. Germans is a candy.

If it hadn't been for the accident to my brother I would have felt simply that every one must fight for his country. Now I say I should hate it. We have plenty of wild flowers. I picked out the littlest poppies. I do not think that bewildering.

Most connections. Most connections consist of eighty-four. Most connections consist of seventy. We were ashamed of the Japanese.

Break away. Break the water.

Powerful James.

The most beautiful spot. This is the most beautiful spot in the world that is according to my idea.

I am not afraid of anything.

Tell me again.

Please help the blind.

Tell me again.

I heard piano playing.

Please tell me again that you heard the playing.

Please tell me again that you like tea.

Do you mean to go.

I mean to go.

I am disappointed in Jenny.

I am not disappointed in Jenny.

He was disappointed in us. We were pleasing.

Are you pleased.

It is favorable.

Sometimes I think that there is a long time in which nothing is happening. Then I say shall we walk. We always answer. Sometimes we are really talkative.

Tonight for example.

Nook.

We took a walk. The light makes that.

No go on.

Every day is reading with eating.

She was very tired and stiff.

Dogs do have a cold nose and a warm nose either. This reminds me of the Irish.

National aspirations. We have the place where a round face and grey eyes where a round face and grey eyes make more recognition of the parting. They part in the middle in the high cart.

Mallorcans please.

Have you ever heard that word.

v.

Your king and country needs you. When I came back to Paris I was surprised not to see these notices up. In Mallorca it was another thing. There was a ring.

I asked if he had ever been in character such a one one who could go in and not in clothing that is to say the right clothing for fighting and he said. I was sick a whole month in Madrid because I knew if I had been born where I could have had the time I would have been successful. He was so seen. We were surprised that he had a brother. He had three of them.

I don't wish to describe a walk.

No.

I don't think so.

Greens and the sea, dark greens. We mention it every night.

Would you like America.

Would you like Switzerland.

Isn't it strange that we should be here.

Catch as catch can.

The kinds of clothes.

A rose is beautiful.

It has green leaves.

So are blue flowers.

If I see a mosquito and I am quick I can destroy it. If I hear it and I am patient I can see it. If I see it twice I can get it. This is my experience. Sometimes I wait longer. It is not true that a dog has instincts. It eats when it is little.

I was pleased to see chocolate which was not of chocolate color. It can roll over.

This is about the war.

Please finish wet.

Please furnish water.

Please furnish water.

All America is solid for the allies.

Mechanics pavilion.

Mechanics pavilion.

Reminded of Mechanics pavilion. Flags of all nations. San Diego.

Please correct this.

Barcelona papers copy.

Stand.

Fair.

I am going to California.

The greatest event in the year seventeen is the restlessness of Roberts. He was restless.

1815.

Niagara.

1815.

Piles of cases.

I love a newspaper.

We will discuss that.

I see what I want to say and I have a very nice time.

I like a little sleep by that time I buy roses. No you don't.

I'd like to go back. Cook knows everybody. I am going to put grease on my face do you mind. A continuance roundness makes a shimmer. I do not like the word basque. I have a prejudice against it and beside I do not desire to have a word changed. This has displeased me. This has not displeased only but it has made me question, was he drunk. There is no use in emergency.

My feeling is about the woman. The boy's name is Bartholomew. The father is Isadore. The mother is changed. She walks slowly. She tells a story. She says that a talent is a thing spent by eating. She means to laugh. By the time she has excused the frenchwoman I no longer listen. I know why I do not like coils. Shawls have hair. Bicycles are skylarks and a silk night has stars and fish nets are bursting, not with fish but with salmonettas. I like frying and I will not be willing. More walls have oak leaves. This sounds like nothing but they are made out of stones. They would do credit to decorations and be witness to a wilderness. Nothing wild rests in Palma. Nothing lonely is poisoned. Nothing discharged is murmured, and loud piles are in the leg. Beat it beat coals of it. Have a gloomy tooth. Shape it by the fire. The fire has stitches and knows how to sew. By all means be with me. Walk faster. Like on the ground and see the cows. Have lots of time. Decide upon a stool. Like soft drinks. Be dazzled.

What are you doing my precious. Taking grease off my face my love.

It is awfully hard not to be a queen.

A slender person growing fatter makes a false cow. Cows are very nice. They are between legs.

I am displeased with Mike.

Dear Dear.

He was right. What is the use of worrying.

He can neglect everything.

By wiping apples by preparing which he makes no mistake by idling, by having a hard answer and by escaping from here by all this he pleases. He pleases me. If you begin as if you were going to stay away and you say this evening, tomorrow is full of solemn thought and Alfred has by nearly a lapse of a deer taught me to swim. I am glad I will not change my mind. This is unsatisfactory.

I enjoyed the book very much. I enjoyed reading it. I was glad to see that they were all happy and that they were miserable those who were capable of spoiling everything. I do not mean that all we were interested in ceased to be gradually or that experience is disheartening, I have learned that I like to go to Palma, reserve my decisions and arrange about shoes. I like to pay for shoes.

I like most of all to be very ready to hear a whistle. I sometimes wonder whether it is a police wheel or contraband being brought to the spot or either of them or perhaps an announcement. I whistle myself. When I do so I mean to attract my attention. I do not laugh. I easily make mistakes. I explain that we are going to Palma. That we wish to get a pair of shoes, that we do not need to be waited for although if we come back we will come in. I say that I will tell it and I do call. Pablo Pablo. This is not the only one of that name. This is not a disappointment or a recollection. I like young turkey. Meat-eater. I saw it come up. Oh very well. When this page is finished they will not smile, they will be angry as ever. This makes war and piling. All of it has language. We spoke very much. I do not like to say it. I believe in weight and diamonds and relief. I believe in examples and ripe nuts. I will pile all the thing together. I broke the pitcher by cracking. This is not the sign of a bill. A little bill.

IV.

I don't drink water.

I'm not your daughter.

Who's having tea. Who. It smells like sea-water. How do you know. By tasting it. I don't like to hear it.

After the war.

Lavender.

Lavender is ferocious.

It grows wild on the hills and we go to see it every day. Sometimes we pick wild honeysuckle. This is when it is veritably here.

What a pleasant sound is coffee. Not when it is on cake. We were not pleased with it but we have decided not to remember our wrongs we have decided to believe in the sun. Dear sun it makes the lamps so black and more than that it makes fishes salmonetta. This is the name of the fish. It is very expensive. It is astonishing. Birds and coffee, birds and coffee make rain. Birds make rain. It is loudly that. I do understand water. Water is of a different kind it has necessity it is obedient, it is warlike, it is selfish, it is freshly undertaken and it is pursued with religion. Mercy and sweetness, fear and authority, dripping, countenance, money, plans, wretched woods, solid pots and rejoicing.

I love alimony by this I mean screaming.

It does smell of pines.

Disturbed.

Disturbed him.

They disturbed him.

Cloth.

Cloths.

They satisfied him.

They alarmed him.

They surprised a brother. They were willing to be agreeable.

It is a strange sound.

Listen.

This is what I have to say.

We said that we would not go out walking.

Mixed.

Mixed with what.

Why surely no language covers it. No right to it.

No plans.

I should think it would hurt the crops.

We have been here a month and a half and have only had two weeks of good weather.

What is shooting.

Shooting is india rubber.

I cannot say that I do not like that. I regard it as finished. Every day I am amazed. More nearly settled. For that reason satisfied. I am inclined to be venturesome, thorough in detail.

I do not like to hear them speak.

Plans.

My plans are that there will not be around any more serpents, not any more dogs or mines, not any liberties. My real feeling betrays me. I am sour.

Oh no.

Let it clap.

Be wise.

Have blue eyes.

Earnest.

Sound and.

Broken.

Tongues speak on Friday.

Chicken which is mistaken for pig.

I told you so.

This is the story.

I ventured to say I reminded diamonds of bridges and clean birds of talking. I said it in song. Instantly there was readiness. They hoped the mother would go.

She did.

It is out of cowardice that I call men tall. Men are tall, they are below that height. They are tall and very earnest. They have every way awaken. Some are mostly languages. Others are shaved. Some are even prayerful and all are muscular. Do be muscular tomorrow. Have feathers made and clouds. Clouds and rain.

I am surprised.

No one would be present.

I am not doing what I want to. This is a phrase.

Jane.

Everybody was in the balconies, some were in the street, some were on the side walk, some were indoors we were sitting, we found it very pleasant and they did not boo the governor.

Crowds of us expected a noise. We were not disappointed. They were not disappointed. We were walking. We walked all the way in.

Anything is a story.

I don't like to walk.

This evening we took a walk not a long walk, we followed the wall, we found the houses looking moorish, after that we had roses, just two and Albert asked us. Albert is the first king, after that everybody is proud. Crowds of water fell, stars shone, gloves were washed and the sun dried it, dried the ground because it was washed away. It was muddy. They said it wasn't.

I do not like the smell of pickles when they are salt pickles. This is a natural prejudice. I do not like hearing it called Fatherland. This is a feeling which will induce me to write about it. I do not wear more. Shoes are enough. I do not wear shoes. I carry a cane. I wear gloves. I sometimes put on a shawl. Sometimes when it is cold I wear woolen stockings. I always have them knitted. By the time we were invited we had had cold weather. We knew what we liked. I can give so many reasons.

The war will not be over. I am following you. First they speak Spanish, this is with that accent, then they change, they address each other. We follow you. Permit me to remain covered. I like that. Many bowed. Some greeted me. All of them were evidently eating their dinner.

We have decided to change the management of this hotel. Four nations have offered to buy it. They expect an answer in two days in that case in three weeks he will undertake it, he will begin by cleaning, after that they will arrange the cooking, then there will be dismissing and I hope they will stay. Do stay. I can see faces clearly. After the war is over.

We were alarmed. Tonight.

We were alarmed. Fishermen can call. They can call on us. We smoke cigarettes. This is an evidence of rapid extension of monopoly. We are so sweet. Moths make a noise. So do piles. So do drawers. So do electric lights. So do matches. Bags make a noise. The little dog was seasick.

My brother went to America.

v.

I am going to tell all my feelings. I love and obey. I am very sensible. I am sensitive to distraction. I like little handkerchiefs. I like to have mosquito netting over my bed. I can estimate the reluctance with which I am hurried. I can understand polish. I like to do my nails. How do I do them. How do you do.

It is easy to be pleased. Regrettable. Circumstance. They make noises. They do this on the roof. Thus they avoid arrest and they continue to be gleeful. They are very simple minded. They admire so much.

We have made a vow never to speak to a german.

Honeysuckle, accacia and roses, they smell together when they are put together. It is our choice to put them together. We found them. They answer this purpose. We are satisfied even pleased.

When it is as big as that it is a fly. I know that by the difference between a fly and a mosquito. A mosquito is a luminous thing it looks just like a castle in the evening.

Every day we are going to go and do something. It would astonish you if we told you about it. Call it a religious procession. Today we saw the cross fall. This being all one had ropes and ropes were untied and held together and holes were not dug deep. I have seen toys like them. Indeed I did in a bottle. The bottle had a cork which was out. This allowed the dirt to settle. The color was not in black or red but fancy blue water. I spoil the name.

We all swam.

If the weather had been warm and I had not known about it I could have been persuaded. Don't say so. You know better. Who is perfect. I know.

Shining.

Jelly.

They do not resemble horses they have the same action and when they fall down they have to be removed from underneath. This explains the pleasures of the handkerchiefs. We all were beside ourselves. We laughed and laughed. We were also enthusiastic.

Nobody need speak of a wilderness. Cows have udders and are very young.

Not to speak of sweating.

Seats and a guard.

I am ashamed.

I have to take care of myself gently.

This is the way we walk. We go first, we stop to speak to an Englishman. In speaking to him we are seated all afternoon. After that we go for a walk. In being lifted over a fence we are happy. We do not tumble. That is because we do not wish to roll stones down if we did we would not be afraid of precipices. We are. Can you say precipitously up or can one only say precipitously down. Can one go up a precipice. Can one admire blue and white streaks or must they always be green and rose color. I do not feel comfortable in a heavy hat. My hat is so light that I do not know when I have it on.

Authority, in speaking of an authority we say he says. We like the phrase in a position to know. We still prefer that the dog looks like a lamb. We change our minds so often. Do not let us worry about it.

Bananas and banana trees. You don't understand me you don't understand the manner of my writing, you do see that here and there there is something to admire. You are convinced of that.

In translating french into English we occasionally say that we will endeavor, we will endeavor to eat.

Sometimes it is not restful.

I don't see how they get accustomed to their hands. After all their faces they don't have to see so much but everybody has to see their hands and I don't see how they get accustomed to their hands. Besides that it is difficult to understand how they can use their hands. How can they use their hands.

I have a pocket full of money.

This is all right because he's here. He tells us about the war. Will Spain come in. Will we feel the benefit of olives that is to say are we right in our predictions. We believe that most people when they make a noise make it with the intention of deceiving. Fishermen can sing.

I do not like stars. I prefer the sky. I sometimes like water. Please be brave.

We intended to pass the day at a respectable procession.

Don't say it.

Fishermen can cook with a fire. They can broil potatoes and onions and mostly in these countries ink is a fish.

Ink is a fish.

Don't be pleasant don't stare, don't be a coward, don't get excited, don't say that we are going walking.

Not amusing.

I will wash my hair.

Not a day.

Three fourths of the time.

I learned pealing. Shall it be said that conversation failed and fanning was necessary and quiet.

This is the way I am going to write.

The war.

Wild boats, wet Saturdays and they gave the order. There is no use in describing. You all know what happened and why we shall be free. In reading about conferences do we plainly state our case. Shall an upper seat where the chickens look so little and yet where there is air shall that by coming early be chosen or shall we choose what we choose. In other words shall we sit. Do tell me, you know very well I never can decide. Shall we walk on. A well informed person is one who reads the papers the newspapers.

Half of an afternoon.

I wanted to be polite.
There is no use in beseeching.
Fans.
Fanning.
Riches.
Sold.
By that.
Splendid.
Old
Walking stick.
Which I did not buy.
Why.
Because it was Mallorcan.
That is the secret.
That is a loud place.
When the sun shines.
Perfect blue water.
Flat.
And not choppy.
When is a wedding.
When is there a wedding.

VI.

An example of fighting. An example in fighting is to be pursued, do not neglect speed and pecking, have plenty of Mondays and say if they are in a green box. This seems like nothing at all but truly it is what we saw. They were the same weight, they came first, we were old, Jenny was delighted.

Was Jenny delighted to stay at home. She certainly would not have enjoyed such a bloody sight.

I don't know when I am disappointed.

We have planned that if the war continues we will go to Malaga after returning to Paris. After that we will go to Seville and Madrid.

Period.

It is not so easy it is not as easy to trick Italy as Greece. I can perfectly understand how it was done. I am not interested in character.

Anybody can be old.

Why say that there is a son-in-law.

A little dog, a dog and its mother. They destroyed pansies. This is historical. I am sadly tormented with flies, I do not mean flies.

This is what is so useless. Lots of talk about Baltimore and butter and New Orleans and flour and Seattle and weather and Richmond and a lottery. A lottery is useless. You easily think of a façade that is in front. Millions are dead. I don't think so.

Please do not make the mistake of singing.

I was so disappointed.

Who was disappointed.

We were so disappointed.

In my case there is that thought.

Ask about two ladies from California.

It is wonderful how I do not succeed in announcing an evening.

I am very tired tonight.

This is the story.

Elvira Lamb was forty years old before she sold tickets. Then she sold lottery tickets. After that she was rich. When she was ten years older she was tall and very good looking and this was not a surprise. Everybody said so. Her father had been trim. He was tall and regular and by that I mean he had a carpet. Carpets are made. They are old or new or light in color or regular in design with a simple center and a continuous border. This was not his character. His son had crutches. He himself was a fighter. He fought by the hundreds. He meant to regard his birthday. After that he was old and eighty. He had plainly manifested a desire not to pry but to be invited. He was not invited to leave a church. No one would be then. This was the sound he made. They all were serious.

His daughter built a house. She was not busy.

Butter cups.

This is not why I am serious. I am serious because I have made a mistake. I really expected supper then when the filet came we were splendid. I said I did not believe in Turkey. Do you remember. Hetty misses faces misses faces most.

Now is the chance.

I meant to say she was my mother. I didn't know how tall the houses were she owned, they might be thirty stories high but anyway she was very rich. They wanted to be polite so they did not ask if she was my sister. One never says that. One does not mention wishing. It is astonishing how often I hear buzzing.

This afternoon we went into Palma. We can read Spanish. All other countries are at war. Dear me. Shoes. Yes they make shoes. The Algerian. Yes she is a woman and a wife. She has a son. His name is Allan. They are rich in Belgium.

What is the matter.

This is a fact. Women have the sense for fact. They can tell about climbing. I mentioned these. It was technically true.

In walking if there is not force there is weight and if there is no hurry there is heat. Moonlight and grape vines, dogs and Japanese. He looks like his brother.

I understand.

Don't worry about moths. If work is well done there is loss and if not there is black wool. There is always some kind of black wool. Be gracious and tuneful and sleep well and have your own way.

How kind.

Fancy leaving alone fancy hurrying, fancy being idle, fancy being courteous, at least insisting on cotton, fancy being polite and serious, I suppose I often suppose that shallow natures are the best.

This would not surprise me.

We were angry with the boundaries. I do not recognize that house. It has a front and back. It has beside a large garden. Be careful to pass it and tell me if there are dogs. Not that I want to enter. I want to ask if there are any french people. I cannot help thinking of war.

This is the end of this chapter.

VII.

A t e eight.

Sign yourself celebrated.

We took a long walk. It was very hot and I perspired freely
My baby has suddenly become very sensitive to light. She explains it by saying that it is hot and so she cannot cover herself
over so as to exclude the light from her eyes. We walked as far
as the powder factory. They say they have enough powder there
to last twenty years. Powder goes bad in two years, it either be-
comes more explosive or loses its explosive character. We found
some new yellow flowers, low bushes of them. We did not have
a knife to cut them. We might have broken them off and we
said we would. We saw a great many sheep. I do not think highly
of natural wool.

We will ask about a hotel in Marseilles. It is splendid to have
a cook. He is fond of fishing. He does not succeed very well. He
has cushions and a friend. This might not be read. What is a
murmur. We do not plan events. We had a long walk today.
We saw the letter. It said that they were street sweepers. They
swept them away like flies. We were very glad to hear it. There
is no doubt about our sentiments. This is as it should be.

Milky way. The translation of this is Saint Augustine.

Do not laugh or relate it to the cow. The cow came out. Of
course it does it has the habit. The next best thing is to sleep
late. Do so.

We were not frightened.

We did not see a religious procession. Don't tell your father
that we did not see a religious procession. Men are courageous.
I could not thinking of meeting a cow in the way of spilling.
Dear me. Men are courageous and Italy is, Italy is in. Dear me.
Why are bulls vexatious. They are not. They run quickly. I
was surprised to be so close out. I put her next to a baby. Leave
us and eat. This is the explanation.

We are going to write to Nelly and ask her to send us wool

and flannel and we are beside that payed well by a boat. A boat makes a whistle. It is dark and by the time oil has been put on bread and chickens are white, they are white, plenty of people eat. Plenty of people do eat.

We reasoned for a lad. That is the way to pronounce. Bottles and bottles of water. I am so sorry. I hope she isn't thinking of it. By the time there was no singing there was music. They asked for it.

Why can I not admire white lilies. We mix them with pink. Lots of houses have food. I often think of it. Italy is in the war. I am so sorry for Sunday. The pope will come to the islands. We will see them together. We will also have tea. We will pour it. Let us not let it satisfy us. Let us celebrate walls.

Cock fighting is a good amusement for shoe-makers.

They have been to the theatre I guess.

What is meat. Rain.

I saw the point of that.

This evening a Belgian dancer and three men came here for dinner. They talked to each other. She had a hat. We did not hear her voice. When they went away she offered to drive the horse. She had given it sugar. One of them said that she did not know the way. Little one he has to get to a paper. Do not delay. This is what they said. It reminded me of the death of Rudolf Habsburg and the wrong blame that was thrown upon Mary Larisch.

I like to hum.

So do I.

Tomorrow we are going to walk.

We can't carry boxes of fruit and prunes around. That's what I say.

It interests me to hear what he has to say. He says do I understand before there is anything to understand and I say yes I understand and then I listen and then I understand. It is easy to understand when it is all about the education of the boy and learning. I wish it were eighty.

Red white and blue.

All out but you.

We have decided to say Viva Italia. This is not wrong. Every one is interested.

Plenty of mines.

Bands of hats.

Straight collars.

Whole pieces.

I was pleased.

I will say this, if he doesn't start when you strike a match on a cement pavement under his nose he won't be shot.

He will not be shot.

We were so pleased with the letter from Eugene Paul.

VIII.

Neglected.

Nobody was neglected.

We were astonished not to receive a letter from Emily. When it came we found that it had been censored. Nothing had been cut and there was not much time lost. Some things are very disturbing.

Lessons of the war.

What this war teaches us. This war teaches us to be certain of our hates. We must clear away boats and hope that somebody is caught. We must not be determined. We must stand to win. We must declare magnanimity to be too great a price to pay for self-respect. We must be courageous. We must surely surround women.

Dancing. Why is dancing bold. Dancing is bold because sorrow is strong. Tears are not able to be removed by water or carnations. This is the term we used to use as pink. Be quick.

We are getting quickly used to the sound of the waves. I have been so disturbed.

I want to tell about the cook fishing. I do not like a description. I can easily see that there is no space. Why should I mean it. I have been led away.

Now let us go back.

This afternoon we went to Buonanova. We did this by ourselves patiently. The sun was shining and beside that there were no birds. Once we hoped to go to the powder factory. We decided it would talk half an hour to go. I do not care to be careful. A soldier salute. This is to say that they are all present to say I will believe in a yellow meadow. I am so disturbed. Calm and bellowing and remind me of Bertha.

I was nervous to expect to clap, I clapped and I could see if I drew my head back. Eyes have that whiteness.

I asked for chicken.

I don't see why they don't love to be in bed. It is disturbing. We wonder why he writes. I do mean everything. I will not have it happen again. No worry. This is the remedy. Expect one evening to close the open door and say it's too close. Then mention the chair say that it obstructs the air. Then the windows are open as they open back. Every one can see the sun. I explained. Sometimes you can hardly tell by that I mean that I have not been deceived. Oh dear. Yes I suffer from it.

I wish to start in this manner. Please me. You please me.

Oh I can't look in every direction. It is only accidentally that I am succeeding so well. What does my hand-writing resemble.

I have been disappointed in measures.

The strongest desire of husband and wife is the welfare of their children.

You can put down whatever address you like.

This evening. This evening we were not annoyed.

Please Pause.

Color of hair.

They described us.

They offered to take us about.

What do I mean by umbrella I mean that I do not wish to purchase a tortoise-shell cane. I would like to go about and see the things that are in windows. Oh yes.

This is what I am accustomed to say, be wakeful have a rocking chair, read the evening paper, not neglectful, having a regard for chickens. I have a regard for turkeys more. I do not like the fashion in which they are arranged. I do not. I consider it a mistake. We were not fooled by the skin. Oh no. We were not.

I was astonished, the violets are sound, they do not have any violets here. They have pink geraniums and this can grow. Well I guess yes. They also are planting some things. In this garden and water.

We are so happy to see, that Pablo there are three Pablos, that Pablo has an appearance of listening. I do not mean that the same name is anything. One of them is willing the other is active and that makes it seem that there is a to-do. I do not know if there is a third. The third is a sailor.

I was not pleased.

If Elizabeth was a girl and it is remarkable that there is a habit in braids all of them have their braids all of them have their braids, we saw some braids. I know thick braids.

Please do not confuse voices with procession, have long callous ways be open and say the prayer. Listen to me sing. I do not mean to be helped. We have concluded that all the presence of Mr. Wilson is necessary to save our way. We hoped to say this. We heard that he was let to have a house in December. Please be with us. I have both.

I could tell all about Spain.

We were awakened by a gun. Thursday is a holiday.

I smell coffee.

Today we went to see a house. It had in it just the kind of decorations I admire. Wall-paper. Real tortoise shell on wood. Door-ways, no hat-boxes and other things, no tables, a house, real silk beds and it happened to be open, the chapel happened to be open. Gardens. What are gardens. I said La France roses. Everybody picked them. We had a pleasant day. We always enjoy it.

Hours, hours of olives.

I taste coffee. I accustom myself to moonlight. Moonlight is the hour when the sympathetic sculptor sees the mountains. He does see most of it. He passes by. A sympathetic sculptor.

We did have shoes.

Why are fine roses not as red as pomegranates. Fine roses are not as red as pomegranates because they have a yellow center.

That is the reason. I can always be proper. I remember what I
see. I saw a whole house and two little things that reminded me
of another, another what, another flower. It was heliotrope. I
said it would do to have heliotrope on the hills. I said it.

Oh no don't come.

I was very pleased.

I cannot endure descriptions.

IX.

Respectable forestry.

Mr. Lerroux held a meeting in Madrid and said, how do
houses grow by every one desiring an addition. What is national
aspiration, national aspiration is thoughtfulness, hair 2, face 2,
teeth 2, dressing, gloves, hat, parlor.

Dental parlor, it was a mistake. I have strange thoughts.

Not too quiet.

Certainly there are three there were only two white and red
ones and there are three. I was not mistaken. I am not mistaken.

We walked in the park. I led the way. We found the road
and went as far as the wall. We went around quite a way and
came back the other side. This is what we did.

I am just as careful.

You always want to let them do it first, allow them to do it
first.

Richard Russell is foolish.

Yes look it up, do look it up.

I am not obliged to remark that I have a failing. It is not
allowable that they change that installation. If they do she will
cry.

Cook me careless, cook me here, cook and lessons, clouds and
times.

Clouds and times.

There is more news in the *Times* than in the New York
Herald. I don't mean that. I am very sorry.

If you wish my influence you have only to say it, to say
that you are active. Why do we admire so those who have no

family fortune. I do. I say that there are earners and savers. I do not like to save, I like to save something, water and strawberries. These are always a disappointment, not water, not strawberries in Toledo.

It is very historical to note that the attack in mass formation was attributed to the germans in the time of Henry the Eighth.

Wretches.

The Wretches.

I could never say I was praised.

Yes it's very important.

I do not wish to be associated with being angry, when I tell him give me a clean napkin I do wish to be angry and I am. I have said I do not remind him to bring me a chair. I have all these troubles.

How do you do I forgive you everything and there is nothing to forgive.

We talk in English.

This was a pause.

Spare me the effort it must be for me to call out my answer. I do not wish to go walking when there is repetition. I wish to ask them do they walk on a flag. I have been told they do. If they do they are not responsible to Spain. This is not surprising seeing that they have some of their own money printed as it is by themselves. They would naturally smoke cigarettes. They do do that. I am so disappointed.

Come again.

A war. A war is a thing where there is a man and a house and practices and leaving. There can also be authorized shellfish, authorized to be old authorized to be sold, language gains, how are seeds and by that time skirmishes. Field lights are those which make out that many of them were astonishing. Dear me. I was not finding it painful. This is war. Wearing is what the mothers say. I have been certainly selfish. Please be so very careful. Have no use for raining. None at all. This is the kind to know. Celebrate me.

I knew I was to blame for that.

Plenty of time.

I am not satisfied with what I do.

A short sharp note.

Oh it was such a pretty color. It was a lobster. I mean one. We had a half. We each had a half.

I am not amused by the sound which I hear which is the sound of water. I am not amused by vertical lines and not thoroughly pleased with their curtains. I do not occupy their chairs. I was not reproachful. I just said I didn't talk French. I was fresh to that. Plans in me were such a quaint relief.

Oh go away.

No man is wicked.

I want to explain about the Spanish. The Spanish want to be recognized. They want air and lungs and festoons. They say as much. They said missed, listen. They said flame misses water, salt water, they said salt water sails bites. They were expectant. Didn't they say they were expectant. I don't do this as well. Good. As good. So. I listen to the dishonesty of the inspection.

This is why we have chosen an island.

I wish I had said bitches. Chocolate is not a bitch. Mary Rose is a bitch if you want but really St. Katherine is full of policemen who sit. Do they. Why do they. They do their duty, and they fail to be torn to pieces. Why do you smile. I don't. I didn't. I smile because Italian and torrential rain, water and bells, turns and rubber shoes are not used any more. I smile at that. It is ridiculous.

Now I am going to tell about stores.

Stores are dark.

I have been so careful.

I will not say what I feel.

X.

You've got to take some risks.

And save some money.

You can't be entirely safe when every country is at war.

There is no need to be worried.

What is a republican.

I don't mean the republican party.

A republican is one who speaking says I am convinced that monarchy is futile. There are some such here. This is not a shock. Fire-arms don't mean a sale and a whole country does not mean over thinly. I wish Pablo were not worried. It is not dangerous to be worried.

Thirty-two, forty, forty-one. Don't sigh.

Clean space.

Clean out.

I saw a church procession. I do mean to say that they walked on the sea only it was heads, just like it.

Boots and a custom.

Just like that by God.

We feel so much.

Not too much.

When we were laughing we were so happy. I can't ask for anything. It is quite satisfactory.

Coo.

Mr. Wilson coos. Don't make any mistake.

We say we are pleased with our meals.

They say they were pleased with their lunch.

Mr. Wilson is not here just now.

I was delighted with the story I read. Anything can happen in a climate which does not necessitate begging. No climate does necessitate begging. This is a thing that is not doubtful. Begging is shameful. Walking on flags is not as it is a proof of disinterested clatter. We did not see it. I chose the word.

It was all my fault that we went too early. If we had gone later we would not have been in time to see them gather. Necessarily we did not stay.

He is always so fortunate.

Not as fortunate as we are. We have several kinds of mineral water.

It is a pleasure.

I can be sure that a time which is prepared is that which I expected.

I like the new chairs.

Why do we like little spots. We do like little spots.

I can easily eat too much. I do not think so.

Please be calming.
Of course you are.
This is the war.

XI.

Of course you are.
Why are holes cool.
All holes are not cool.
Some holes are cool.
Can I mention an exceptional one.
They have written to me about a great deal.
They mention purchases.
This is a story.
He was the brother of the sister of the secretary of state and
he stole all the money and he stayed in dirty water. He escaped.
He came to build houses. He built a hotel too and factories. He
gave the key to no one in the door and he said his wife owned
it. Now he is poor and lives in Terreno. Do you know how to
pronounce it. You can never tell who is a republican.
     Another one was earnest in one. He had a house and terri-
tory. He was pleased. Now he is beside that. He belongs to the
aristocracy.
     I do not care to mention him.
     I cannot tell it to you because he will understand.
     I have deliberately refrained from referring earlier to the
Empress Victoria. In walking we passed a house where the dog
came out. He did not relieve the standing. He stood to be a
Negro. I do not mean dirt. Nobody could.
     Let me say America. Nobody knows so much. Nobody
knows as many kinds of Americans as my friend does. He tells
me kindly. Senators are speechless. Angry speeches. A clause
asking what are carpets. Then six feet. Are six feet peculiar.
Should they not be considered. Is it not careful to measure. Certainly he did. He was secure. He was sure. He did measure. He
measured arms. I like all kinds. Fishermen take lights in a room
they take lights into a room.
     This is a test.

We were not angry.

In reading a description of Russian mines we were obliged to be thankful we were thankful for all the oaths. We swore our way. We said leave us. We did not say spectacle. This is serious. Do talk to strangers.

Mr. Wilson. It is natural to burn. It is natural to save us. It is natural. I declare. I believe he has gone. Mr. Wilson has gone it will take him 5 days to get to England. His mother is ninety-one.

Mr. Wilson's friends. Two ladies. Englishwomen, they have been staying at William and now they need a change. They don't need to leave soon but they will they will, they speak English.

The war. I am not disappointed in the war. Some are. I am not. I have a great deal of faith in Mrs. Stone. Not exactly. I said Mrs. Stone. Of course I don't mention dates. Feeling this. I do feel strange. I have no way to walk. I walk with me.

XII.

Seven more chapters and then we will begin something new.

What did you want me to mention, oh yes, I don't remember. I don't remember either what the name was that was the Count's name. I don't remember that either. I am very sleepy.

Cause a word. Because a word. By smiling. This is really cross.

A lesson. Electric roads. I said that we manufactured for our own country. I now say that we sell to Spain. I don't care. I could easily say that.

Please be rich.

Clarence.

Clearance.

Puget Sound.

Seattle.

Bay.

No mosquitoes at all.

I will not make a short paragraph.

I did laugh.

Describe.

Plenty of pump. Of course the water.

Very different.

No Barbarity it is called.

Listen to it.

Hear me.

We were wondering.

I don't mean by that that we were patient. Let us give this name Jenny excellent here. Do not mistake which Jenny. No I will not. I make no mistake. I don't think I would I don't believe Henrietta would let me.

I did help her.

I very warm room.

I understand Maddalena's feelings a little bit. After all she moves her hand and there is no excitement and then why should you be tired not be tired. She says this is what happened. In getting off the tramway which is a street car she fell and was seen and the young man who is in a position here picked her up. He was very careful. He told her to hold him to his memory of what he had seen. He was disturbed. Not by the event. He had disinfectant in a bottle which was mineral. The water was mineral. He explained it, he said it was the bottle, the bottle was mineral water and that was not disinfectant there was disinfectant in that bottle. The inspector of the line came in to see and ask whose fault was it. This was the way he put it, whose fault was it. He was not harsh. He was not deceiving. He was a maker of chairs and he had a hat. He went away. The cook by and by the cook had water, he it was who had assistants. Then the waiter, then indeed the employer and the lady who did not wish to see or suffer. She did not mind coughing. She never hated. She said I will do so. It is explained. Don't bother me. Do you remember the looks of the woman who had two children. Of course you do. Some women have altogether no sense for fact I meant to say laughing. Yes they laugh. Please credit me. We are all asleep. At least it is cooler tonight.

I am not very delighted with self lighting cigarettes, all the conductors were but they found them too expensive. They smoke eleven cigarettes up or down and that makes more than fifty in all as they are at work eighteen hours. That would make

many more than fifty, that would make a hundred and fifty.
They smoke a hundred and fifty a day.

Breathing, dear thing.

We have a house now that I am delighted.

It is not argumentative, I am not good at argument I can
study for that. I had better not say about flowers and filling up
with roses. She will decide.

This is the most exciting thing they have destroyed a Zeppelin. He has destroyed a Zeppelin.

I was astonished I was astonished at her letters. By, can you
say by.

Anything you look at is impulsive.

Skip that.

I will go on sir.

Seventeen as well as eighteen hours.

XIII.

Friendship.

Please leave slippers.

For me.

It was a surprise.

That isn't his name.

There.

There we are.

The long life.

Of Mabel Digby.

The youth.

Of Henry the Eighth.

You expect fifteen you don't expect twelve or thirteen.

Oh dear don't bother me.

A history of our walk.

We started.

We went to the new house.

We were pleased.

We went on a little way.

We turned around.

We decided not to go to see a dog.

We said we agreed.
Then what.
We went everywhere.
We were hot.
We sat down.
It was very pleasant.
We said we were happy.
We were more than happy.
We were delighted.
We did omit to change our shoes.
I didn't.
We didn't.
We came in then.
We both slept some.
This is quiet.
Very quiet.
We were so agreed.
We were so pleased.
We were pleased with the sun.
We were pleased with warming.

Yes we were.
We will like our new house.
Is there artificial light in here. I don't understand.
Yes you do.
Alright then.
We are going to swim.
Are we so.
Yes.
And
No.
That's it.
We don't have to sign the inventory.
We are not afraid.
Of thunder.
And lightning.
And bombs.
We are glad of the rain.

We wish for flowers.

There is rain.

It is raining.

You don't find it suggestive.

We are all sleepy.

I breathe in a place where there is pink and red color and I intend to buy it. We did. She came out to the floor. She was a big woman and had a son and yet her husband came home. Were we downhearted. We were not. We said we could go to the market. Geraniums and carnations can be gotten in the market but tube-roses, I am not sure about tube-roses. Dear me Dear me. Which is it. That's right. Say it. Dear me Dear me.

Like again like it again.

That's very good.

She will accept the salary they may earn by mending their own clothes.

He was funny.

Oh gracious they do seem to get bigger all the time.

That's nothing.

I read Spanish words hastily.

She couldn't talk Breton, she doesn't talk french she talks the language that was handed down to her.

Her daughter is satisfied with eating.

The Heart of Beef.

Rich men and titles.

Kind.

Sea-bathing.

Not amber beads.

I will be through soon.

I know what I like.

XIV.

Spiraea is the name of that tree Spiraea not Wisteria.

Sunday night, monday night tuesday night wednesday night.

That's all.

Be a brave example and don't mind the mosquitoes.

Why do we stay on the island. We have several reasons. It is inexpensive, money is easily gotten and there are no victims. They all speak the language.

There is Algeria.

There is the Algerian.

There is a Belgian and a doctor.

There are no more consuls except 45. They each are aware of the world. Do be aware of it. We climbed a hill. We climbed on a hill.

Marie Rose and Chocolate pronounced french.

We will have a puppy.

Yes Miss.

We talked to a man from San Francisco who had a nurse. He was sick. He had been to the West Indies and had a colored nurse. He had been in Mexico. He had intended to go to the Holy Land but he had trouble in England on account of their checking system that is to say his luggage was not on the boat. He is now going on to Italy. Later he will get to Madeira where his mail is waiting for him.

We are not patient.

Today we bought quite a number of flower plants.

We also bought towels.

The man who was the son said he knew a man who was in the business of selling mineral water. If we intended to get it by the case he could get it for us as cheaply as the central pharmacy.

I do not understand the thing. Why do stockings come down in hot weather. There is an explanation. I do not know it.

Plan it.

You don't know it but you must be careful with your water. Use it use all you want of it but be careful with it. What you have you keep back. Not that there is any danger of not having enough, there isn't but I'd be a little careful and use it. Use all you need, after all there is always enough. Anyway you won't have any trouble.

A BIRTHDAY BOOK

(1924)

BIRTHDAYS.

Who was born January first.
Who was born in January first.
Who was born and believe me who was born and believe me,
who was born who was born and believe me.
At that rate.
Let us sell the bell.

Who was born and believe me for this reason, this reason the
reason is that the second of January as the second or January,
February or the second or January, he was born and believe me
the second of January. The second of January as the second of
January.

The third.
The third.
The third might be might it might it be might the third be
the third of January.
Might it be the third anyway, might it be the third of Jan-
uary anyway.
Run so might it be the third might it run so that it would be
January and the third and the third and January and run so. The
third of January.

Fourth of January reminds one of something reminds one of
the fourth. The fourth of January reminds one the fourth of
January and so forth, and so fourth and January. More January.
More slowly. More slowly fourth more slowly January fourth.

Fifth no one born.

Sixth no one born.
Sixth no one born.
Fifth no one born.

Fifth and sixth no one born.
No one born fifth and sixth no one born.
January fifth and sixth no one born.

January seventh.
As well known as January seventh.
And approach.

January eighth and an approach. Such an approach.

January ninth and nicely.
Approach.

January tenth just the same. It is just the same.

January eleventh respectively.

January twelfth may be yes.
In January can't they in January they can.

In January they can can't they.
Understood thirteen.

January fourteenth and just at noon.
How early in the day can any one be born.

January fifteenth and can they.

January sixteenth and the rest a day.

January seventeenth any day. Any day and dressed a day.
Any day and undoubtedly as it may be.

January eighteenth more easily used to be it.

January nineteenth merely in the meantime. In the meantime
and they will anyway.
January nineteenth celebrated on the seventeenth.

January twentieth has to go as prepared. Prepared as it is. All of it integrally shown and as to the hearing.

January twenty-first and to it. Do not forget birthdays. This is in no way a propaganda for a larger population.

January twenty-second and twenty-second. January twenty-second and twenty-second. January twenty-second and twenty-second.

January twenty-third not as wanted. January twenty-third as wanted not as wanted. January twenty-third for January the twenty-third.

January the twenty-fourth makes it as late, as late as that.

January the twenty-fifth ordinarily.

January the twenty-sixth as ordinarily.

January the twenty-seventh January twenty-seventh signed January the twenty-seventh.

January the twenty-eighth and August.

January the twenty-ninth as loudly.

January the thirtieth to agree, to agree to January the thirtieth.

January the thirty-first usually. Used. Usually. Usually. Used.

Thirty-one won.
Thirty-one won.
Thirty and one and won one.
Thirty-one won thirty-one won thirty-one thirty-one thirty-one won. Won. One. Thirty-one.

February first. First. At first.

February second this second.

February third Ulysses. Who Ulysses. Who Ulysses. Who Ulysses.
February third. February third heard word purred shirred heard. Heard word. Who.

February fourth. Get in, oh get in.

February fifth. Any and many, many and any. Any more.

February sixth, a mixed and mixed.

February seventh and so forth.
February seventh and so forth.
February seventh and so forth and February seventh.

February eighth oh how do you do.

February ninth collectedly, so collectedly, as collectedly.

February tenth makes eating easy, or easily. As February tenth makes it easy or easily.

February eleventh. Not is dishes. Dishes are named Emanuel or Rosita.

February twelfth consider it at all.

February thirteenth, more difference.

February fourteenth, when this you see remember me and you will anyway.

February fifteenth. Have you had it have you had it have you had it as you had it as you had it have you had it have you had it as you had it have you had it.

February sixteenth. So much so.

February seventeenth has a married lady. Married. Lady.

February eighteenth. Has it.

February twentieth. Excuse me.

February nineteenth. I agree you agree you agree I agree I agree you agree lily agree lily or three.

February twenty-first, pronounce as at first pronounce and as at first or at first, pronounce it first.

February twenty-second was mentioned.

February twenty-third. A chicken lies in or win or what it lies in.

February twenty-fourth, for a four, four leaf for or four, four leaf four leaf for four leaf or four leaf for for a leaf. Four leaf. For four leaf.
February twenty-fourth. As a wife has a cow entitled.

February twenty-fifth. Twenty days as days.

February twenty-sixth. Twenty days also twenty days.

February twenty-seventh has a place in history. Historical and so near.

On the twenty-eighth of February in and win always so prettily.

Washing away, every day.
Equally an undiscovered country so.
Every other day they may say pay.

March at one march at once march at one march for once.

March the second wedding march march or rain, and do march, march marble, marbles march.

March the third or church.

March the fourth or churches.

March the fifth or powder.

March the sixth or giggling.

March the seventh patently, patently see, patently saw, she saw he saw patently see to see. He would be.

March the eighth, jumping and picking up the purse, jumping up and picking up the purse.

March the ninth. Does it weigh.

March the tenth. Successively stay.

March the eleventh. The door.

March the twelfth. Some more.

March the thirteenth. Some more explore some more, as before as explore some more.

March the fourteenth. The weather otherwise.

March the fifteenth. Did the rest.

March the sixteenth and many.

March the seventeenth added addition.

March the eighteenth may we blame no one and in this way reconcile ourselves to every obligation.

March the nineteenth formerly not at all and now nearly as contentedly nearly as candidly nearly as swimmingly nearly as neglected, not as neglected as at all and so forth.

March the twentieth melodrama.

On March the twenty-first it is our duty to call a halt.

On March the twenty-second likewise.

And on March the twenty-third witnesses.

March the twenty-fourth able to be able to be able very able he is very able he is a very able man.

March the twenty-fifth makes it up.

On March the twenty-sixth it is made up to them everything is made up to them it is made up to them for everything.

March the twenty-seventh to declare and is it so. March the twenty-sixth declare and is it so. Is it so and March the twenty-sixth and declare and is it so.

March the twenty-seventh ordinarily. Ordinarily on March the twenty-seventh an added restraint likewise makes itself felt.

March the twenty-eighth ordinarily on March the twenty-eighth ordinarily as added as an objection.

March the twenty-ninth for instance.

March the thirtieth makes March the thirtieth makes March the thirtieth and makes, makes March the thirtieth and makes March and makes March the thirtieth.

March the thirty-first reasonably.

April the first, yes sir.

April the second in order to maintain that this would be especially so.

April the third every once in a while.

On April the fourth use your brush and comb use your comb and brush.

April the fifth rush.

April the sixth if you like it say you do.

April the seventh cook and stew as you do as you used to do as you are used to as you are used to it.

April the eighth master-pieces fairly surely surely carefully carefully entirely, entirely fairly fairly carefully carefully surely surely carefully.

April the ninth or choose it as carefully.

April the tenth happened to say.

April the eleventh as the one said.
April the eleventh as the one said and as they and as the one said.

April the twelfth fed it yesterday they fed it yesterday.

April the thirteenth when there is more or less in the meantime.

April the fourteenth ought it to be caught ought it to be.

April fifteenth as if it ought to be taught ought it to be taught, ought it to be taught as it ought to be.

April the sixteenth waited till it was finished before she budged.

April the seventeenth on April the seventeenth really really on April the seventeenth and really, on April the seventeenth usually next to it.

April the eighteenth has interested me.

April the nineteenth fourteenth the fourteenth nineteenth, April nineteenth, the fourteenth April nineteenth the fourteenth.

April twentieth makes a movement.

April the twenty-first shall it be April the twenty-first, asked to be has to be has to be asked to be asked to be April the twenty-first has asked to be April the twenty-first.

April the twenty-second not mentioned in history.

April the twenty-third and they see the point. Do they see the point.

April the twenty-third and was it.

Was it April the twenty-fourth was it.

It was April the twenty-fifth and was it on April the twenty-fifth and how was it on April the twenty-fifth.

To be to the twenty-sixth of April it is to be to the twenty-sixth of April it is to be the twenty-sixth of April as it is to be the twenty-sixth of April as it is to be. It is to be until it is the twenty-sixth of April.

The twenty-seventh of April coming nearer.

And the twenty-eighth of April which is so exciting.

The twenty-ninth of April so reasonably is the twenty-ninth of April is so reasonably as reasonably as it is.

The thirtieth of April selects selects the thirtieth of April. As it selects the thirtieth of April, as it selects. Selects the thirtieth of April. Sell it selects. Selects see ordered.
Thirty days has September April June and November.
May and might hold me tight, might and may night and day, night and day and anyway, anyway as so gay, gayly, gayly misses.

May day.

Second of May, second of May yes sir.

Third of May means that there is enough that there is enough the third of May and enough.

The fourth of May enough and enough and the fourth of May.

The fifth of May and so much to be said for it.

And the sixth of May has exactly for the sixth of May there is exactly on the sixth of May exactly as on the sixth of May anyway.

The seventh of May easily.

The eighth of May as easily.

The ninth of May may may.

The tenth of May may be. On the eleventh of May may be they will be there.

The eleventh of May as is necessary all the time.

The twelfth as it is necessary all the time.

The thirteenth of May on the thirteenth of May as expected next time on the thirteenth of May.

On the fourteenth of May expect on the fourteenth of May.

The fifteenth of May expect next time expected next time, next time.
The fifteenth of May gradually.

Sixteenth of May gradually the sixteenth of May.

The seventeenth of May is the day on that day on that day is their day.

The eighteenth of May yesterday. A disappointment.

The nineteenth of May nearly as much of an advantage as ever.

Every yours as always sincerely yours yours truly and on the twentieth of May as dated.

The twenty-first of May as stated.

The twenty-second of May as if it were as an assembly.

The twenty-third of May as much as there is to do and able to go through to as in stretches as they do.

On the twenty-fourth autograph on the twenty-fourth may they photograph on the twenty-fourth as the twenty-fourth of May.

The twenty-fifth minus the other numbers, May the twenty-fifth and minus the other numbers.

The twenty-sixth in addition.

The twenty-seventh for division.
The twenty-seventh of May, May, for subtraction, the twenty of May, May, for subtraction. The twenty-seventh of May, May, for subtraction.

The twenty-eighth of May as the result of learning.

The twenty-ninth of May in various places.

The thirtieth of May or we have it as we have it.

On the thirty-first of May remember titles on the thirty-first of May remember titles to what on the thirty-first of May remember titles on the thirty-first of May as remember titles. Little single since.

The first of June. Smile. When you see me smile. When do you see me smile. As you see me smile. Smile while mile afterwards. Smile mile while afterwards.

June the second as favorably as that as June the second as favorably as that.

And interlude between June and July and July and August. Red Indian fed Indian wed Indian said Indian. He said In-

dian. He said Indian red Indian fed Indian wed Indian she wed
Indian. Wed Indian fed Indian said Indian red Indian, she said
red Indian. Red Indian said Indian wed Indian fed Indian she
said wed Indian. She said red Indian. She said fed Indian. She
said fed Indian wed Indian red Indian, she said red Indian.

Shall I use that for a month or a day, to us who gave you a
day.

June the third has many times three, three four not any more
two three as can be one two as you, one won.

June the fourth methodically.

June the fifth two and two nicely.

On June the sixth as it happened again and was sustained too.

June the seventh very likely to be very well arranged.

June the eighth upper eat upper and ate upper and on finding
and likely to be very well arranged.

June the ninth and nicely and as well arranged.

June the tenth for instance is there more is there very much
more.

June the eleventh for instance.

June the twelfth if finding makes a difference.

June the thirteenth if in inattention, June the thirteenth if as
well as they all know it, if in inattention, if as well as they all
know it if in inattention and if as well as they all know it.

On June the fourteenth avail and too much in contribution.

The fifteenth of June and seasoned.

The sixteenth of June and habitually has habitually, it was habitually.

The seventeenth of June measured by this.

The eighteenth of June in on receipt.

The nineteenth of June was as always.

The twentieth of June changed by letter.

The twenty-first of June as an instance, instance of what instance of exactitude.

The twenty-second and on the twenty-second of June.

June the twenty-third, originally originally June the twenty-third.

June the twenty-fourth. This time the wives will sign. Today the wives will sign.

June and so forth. June the twenty-fifth, June the twenty-fifth. June and so forth.

June the twenty-sixth her name is June and very very soon.

June the twenty-seventh June and just as soon just as soon as just as soon.

June the twenty-eighth and just as soon.

June the twenty-ninth here and there a name.

June the thirtieth and here and there and the same here and there. Here and there a name.

Thirty days has September April June and November here

and there a name all the same. All the same here and there a name all the same all the same a name here and there.

July because because July because because July because.

July the first because July the first. July the first because.

July the second jealously.

July the third in a place in the place in the place of it.

July the fourth as everybody as a sample as a sample as everybody.

July the fifth come too come to places come to places come as comfortably.

On July the sixth the understanding which means only here and there that only there which means that, only here and there.

July the seventh in the meantime it is pointed out.

July the eighth in which house did he live.

July the ninth ineradicably.

July the tenth makes August and September.

July the eleventh a puzzle.

July the twelfth ought to be ought to be ought to be all that it ought to be.

July the thirteenth in which house did he live.

July the fourteenth July the fourteenth fifty, July the fourteenth thirty, July the fourteenth thirty July the fourteenth fifty. July the thirteenth fifty and thirty.

July the fifteenth the day of delivery.

July the sixteenth is historical.

July the seventeenth November September October December.

July the eighteenth on July the eighteenth it is the same thing or July the eighteenth it is the same thing.

July the nineteenth before Mary.

July the twentieth before Mary Rose.

July the twenty-first before Mary Louise.

July the twenty-second an emergency.

July twenty-third July twenty-third for this and before this and because of this.

July twenty-fourth period.

July the twenty-fifth is easily replaced.

And July the twenty-sixth still more easily.

July the twenty-seventh is not simply prepared for.

July the twenty-eighth. Fanny has a market.

July the twenty-ninth to please and please.

July the thirtieth ministrations.

July the thirty-first the first.

August and and August and and August and and August.

August first and foremost.

August the second there where there were there. Where.

August the third as may be said so.

August the fourth then I would like to like to very much.

August the fifth then to like to like to very much.

August the sixth to forget in which house did he live.

August the seventh unable to.

August the eighth all August the eighth.

August the ninth at that.

August the tenth tenth ten times August the tenth, tenth time the tenth time.

August the eleventh. To you who who to you.

August twelfth that is a nice one.

August the thirteenth and that is a nice one.

August the fourteenth forget in which house did he live.

August the fifteenth was understood to be principally for them all.

August the sixteenth on August the sixteenth usually unusually so.

August the seventeenth usually unusually prompt.

August the eighteenth unusually so.

August the nineteenth it is felt to be.

August the twentieth conviction the conviction that there is August the twentieth illustrates very well this occasionally.

August the twenty-first illustrates this occasionally.

No August the twenty-second, the second.

August the twenty-third as illustration of this occasionally.

August the twenty-fourth for the fourth time as a fourth. As a fourth. August the twenty-fourth.

August the twenty-fifth the fourth of what.

August the twenty-sixth and perfumery and stationery.

August the twenty-seventh for instance.

August twenty-eight a date. Date palm date of harm date of harm date farm. Farming.

August the twenty-ninth needless to say.

August the thirtieth thirty day August the thirtieth thirty days and August the thirtieth and the thirty days. And the thirty days, following. And the thirty and the days and following.

August the thirty-first for in a way.

September first because in a way.

September the second because in a way.

September the third house them, a house, house them arouse, house explanation.

September the fourth and as finally and as house to house and as house to house and as finally.

September the fifth formerly finally.

September the sixth formerly finally and as house to house and a house to house and as formerly finally.

September the seventh for that reason.

September the eighth in which house did he live formerly.

September the ninth and in which house did he live.

September the tenth or formerly a great deal.

September the eleventh on September the eleventh interested in birthdays.

September the twelfth as meant to be September the twelfth.

Interested in birthdays on September the thirteenth and this without principally.

September fourteenth measured measured September the fourteenth.

September fifteenth equal and as a cow.

September sixteenth anyhow.

September the seventeenth has remarkably few.

On September the eighteenth as they knew.

September the nineteenth wintergreen.

September the twentieth winter and green.

September the twenty-first no dates mentioned.

September the twenty-second thirty days has September.

September the twenty-third April June.

September the twenty-fourth and November.

September the twenty-fifth all the others.

September the twenty-sixth thirty-one.

September the twenty-seventh except the second.

September the twenty-eighth the second.

September the twenty-ninth month alone.

September the thirtieth but a year.

September a year gives it twenty-nine.

October in fine.

October first gives it twenty-nine.

October second gives it twenty-nine in fine.

October the third conscientiously.

October the fourth how many and changes.

October the fifth foremost and first.

October the sixth at first.

October the seventh one two three.

October the eighth one two three four five six seven.

October the ninth at first.

October the tenth eleven at first.

October the eleventh ten at first.

October the twelfth on which account.

October the thirteenth can it can it come, come and can it can it come, for instance come, for instance can it.

October fourteenth can it come for instance.

October fifteenth eight a day two a day two a day as eight as eight.

October sixteenth as eight, two as two, eight as eight, eight as eight a day.

October seventeenth not to hurry.

October eighteenth finally for it.

October nineteenth on October the nineteenth on October the nineteenth on and over.

October the twentieth makes it sound so.

October the twenty-first and may be yes.

October the twenty-second finally October the twenty-second.

October the twenty-third, in a minute.

October the twenty-fourth for October the twenty-fourth or for October the twenty-fourth.

October the twenty-fifth sounds like a half.

October the twenty-sixth not again.

October the twenty-seventh and not again.

October the twenty-eighth and not as as not and not again and not as, as it.

October the twenty-ninth arithmetic, follow me, arithmetically.

October the thirtieth as slowly as October the thirtieth.
October the thirtieth and in reference to it, as as and and and and and as as. As as, as and as and, as and, and as.
October the thirtieth makes three numbers.

October the thirty-first necessary and not, and not and not and necessary and not. November to repeat. Repeat November November November. Easy to repeat. Easy to repeat November, not as easy, not so easy not to repeat November and first.

November first. First and ferries. Ferries, to go across ferries.

November the second. Cross he looks.

November the third across the end across the end and where to cross the, and where is it.

November the fourth where is it.

November the fifth what is the what is it.

November the sixth when and when and as and as, as readily.

November the seventh when and when and there and there and as readily.

November the eighth and as readily.

November the ninth slightly as now.

November the tenth furnished anyhow.

November the eleventh where and where, how and how, now and now, neither.

November the twelfth. Early or, ore, this is sold.

November the thirteenth and Tuesday.

November the fourteenth happily November the fourteenth.

November the fifteenth in fifteen.

November the sixteenth or sixteen.

November the seventeenth makes a mail a day.

November the eighteenth let us.

November the nineteenth very vary very.

November the twentieth stretches.

November the twenty-first stretches further.

November the twenty-second and ministrations over again.

November the twenty-third fortunately.

November the twenty-fourth more fortunately.

November the twenty-fifth most fortunately.

November the twenty-sixth mostly.

November the twenty-seventh and now.

November the twenty-eighth four more.

November the twenty-ninth as hindered.

November the thirtieth thirty days, thirty days as. As and has.

December springing spring and sprung.

December the first strung.

December the second strong.

December the third stronger.

December the fourth surely and also.

December the fifth to change for it.

December the sixth to change for it.

On December the seventh she lost a newspaper.

December the eighth where as nearly.

December the ninth when as soon.

December the tenth when as soon.

December the eleventh where as nearly.

December on the twelfth of December where and when.

On the thirteenth of December where and when as nearly as
soon.

On the fourteenth of December and to remember it as such.

On the fifteenth of December as an organization.

December sixteenth as meant.

December seventeenth and may do.

December the eighteenth if to witness.

December the nineteenth may do it too.

December the twentieth as it would would it.

December the twenty-first colored by and by.

December the twenty-second as he said.

December the twenty-third to scatter.

December twenty-fourth minstrels to mean even.

December twenty-fifth and always interested in birthdays.

December twenty-sixth and may do too.

December twenty-seventh have time.

December twenty-eighth a million.

December twenty-ninth or three.

December thirtieth corals.

December thirty-first. So much so.

DAHOMY

OR

AS SOFT A NOISE (A SERIAL)

(1924)

Gody is short for Godiva and Goddy is short for god-son.
What kind of things do you break.
Excuse me.
What kind of things do you break.
And what kind of things do you break.
This all introduces all of it.
First as a family.
Second as a family.
Third as a family.
Fourth as also a family.
First case a husband and wife and two daughters.
Second case a husband and wife and a grown up son and a friend and her adopted child.
Third case a husband a wife and pleasure.
Fourth a husband and wife and present.
In each case they come together practically all the time when they come they come as they come together practically all the time.
Incredible. Nothing is incredible if the description of it is just the same as it was when the noise of it four and fourteen. She can count to fourteen.
A detailed exposition with descriptions of what they do.
Pleasurably in an analysis of pleasurably. This is seen in an analysis of pleasurably.
This is seen in an analysis of pleasurably.
Not easily at all.
First, thought she was foolish.
Second thought of it.
Second thoughtfully.
A first. He was the first.
She thought he was foolish. As foolish as that. She thought it was foolish. He thought it was foolish. She thought it was as foolish as that.

Nearly a mistake, he nearly made a mistake, he was mistaken.

She very nearly felt very well and at first as she felt very well she felt it to be very well arranged. Purely stationary. It was purely fresh and clean, it was very properly there, here and there and least of all neglected. A reason for it to be so.

Imagine a very little and a great many others. Imagine a very little and imagine a great many others. Imagine a great many others and imagine very little imagine very little and imagine a great many others a great many others imagine very little and imagine very little and imagine and a great many and a great many others. Progressively.

This makes disappearance equal to disappearance.

This makes disappearance equal to disappearance.

Four families, four families many fairly well.

Four families many fairly well if they may say so.

Four families many fairly well and four families many fairly well.

Four families many fairly well.

Mentioned. In the meantime. More at home. Once. In the meantime mentioned once. Once more mentioned in the meantime, it was mentioned once more in the meantime. In the meantime it was mentioned once more in the meantime. It was mentioned once more in the meantime it was mentioned once more.

Which, several, which several, which several, as several which, which several. Several serial which, which serial which, several which, which serial which. Which serial. Which serial.

Four families may fairly well, which four families may fairly well which serial, which, serial. Four families which, four families serial four families very well.

Very well.

Four families.

Which.

Very well which.

Which very well.

Four very well.

Several very well.

Which several very well fairly well, which fairly well.

Four families.

The first family which very well, very well which, several very well, fairly well, which fairly well very well which the first family which very well, several very well several which very well several very well. Very well.

The first family was very well, several very well. The first family which was very well several were fairly well. Which family.

The second family very well the second family.

Serially the third family. The third family several several and very well.

The fourth family several and the fourth family, well, well the fourth family very well the fourth family.

A family and fairly well, well fairly well and please wind the clock and is it happily is it happily. As happily as it could be. Four families make four. Four families and four more. Four more families and four more. Four more families.

The first family has unquestionably roses and roses. The second family unquestionably has suggestions. The third family unquestionably varies. The fourth family has unquestionably more reason.

At first the first on the first, on the first at first, first of all, the first of all was this that they had no reason to make to give to give to have, they had a reason to give for this. The reason they had to give was this that they should marry and having married should one having married should one choose between going and coming. Coming and going and so forth.

In the second place imagining it to be only once. Once and for all and so forth. If it was left over it was left over and over.

In the third place once in a while once in a while and very often and most of it in place in the place of it.

Fourthly for distribution distributed right and left.

Formerly for for formerly and for. Not if another way much, otherwise, very much.

When Lily and Edna and Clara and Hilda and Arthur and Frank and William and Frederick and Sylvia and Ada and Inez and Hilda and Edith and William and Herbert and Eva and Mary and Harriet and Estelle and Clarence and George and Howard and Geoffrey when after all all told they are after all

all told twenty. Beginning with half of it. Ten. Beginning with more of it. Twelve. Beginning with half of it. Six. Instantly there is a difference.

Beginning advantageously.

As forty is to twenty and furthermore.

In one family as one family as a family as a family fairly well as a family and they were very nearly fairly well as a family. In the mean time all four lived in Oakland. All four lived in Oakland all four lived in Pont de Cheri all four lived in Oakland and all four lived in Pondicherry. All four lived in Oakland all four lived in Pondicherry all four lived in Oakland all four lived in Oakland all four lived in Pont de Cheri. All four lived in Oakland. All four families lived in Brooklyn, all four families lived in Piedmont all four families lived in Wales all four families lived in Switzerland all four families lived in Oakland all four families lived at home. All four families all four as families all four families all four families were fairly well all four families. All four families and fairly well and all four as families and all four families.

Nevertheless all four families.

One family, in following in following as has been followed. They were following and they have been following before before this.

More than that. Two more than that. Two more than that make of it as they have to have it. As they have to have it. The first family reasonably, reasonably chooses reasonably chooses more reasonably chooses more reasonably chooses as more reasonably chooses as more and reasonably chooses and as reasonably and as they more reasonably and as they as reasonably as they choose and as they choose as they as reasonably as they choose.

The second family as chosen to chose makes and made to choose made and choice and chosen and for instance.

The third family remarkably clearly as fortunately as a fact.

The fourth family pursues the fourth family pursues pursues for which pursues for which and formerly pursues and formerly, pursues and for which, and for which and pursues formerly all make all also, all also all make all also all make also all also all make. All also all make all also.

Fourteen as seen.

If brown if it is brown if she cannot remember if she cannot remember the color of her sister's ideas and she saw her sister yesterday does she know if brown does she know if it is brown does she know brown and blue does she know if it is brown does she know as brown does she know as blue does she know that her sister has does she know that her sister has to have and does she know it is it brown is it brown and does she have to have it and does she have it and has she it too.

The next family organizes.

As the next family has more nearly had a part of it here and there.

The next family proceeds to be so.

And so and the next family and so.

Funnily enough and the next family and so and so and funnily enough and the next family and so and funnily enough.

Is it necessary that they know that the son and so is it necessary that they know so and so.

Three things settled climate geography and origin. Three things more that are settled temperature contributions observations and as many times more.

One one as much one as much as that.

One as much as that.

The first time as a first time readily.

As a second time as a second time as twenty.

As a third as a third time as surely.

As a fourth time as a fourth time or two.

A family makes more necessary that the two as sisters leave earlier and as they must go quickly they may have to leave at once.

The second time a second time shows it shows how clearly how clearly it is how it is so very clearly there.

The third time more is mentioned.

And the fourth time it mounts up.

It mounts up to this it amounts to this, it amounts to this

that not a little more that a little more that necessarily a little more that a little more is as necessary as that.

So many separate cases. There is silver in so many different cases, there is silver in so many separate cases.

If a bird as a bird if a sister as a sister if a son as a son if a son if a godson, and settled to that.

If as it can if it can be as it can and if arrangements are made if arrangements are to be made how can they at least offer it now.

If when it went very well it was certain to be so it was certainly to be so more so.

If all the more if all the more if they all the more if they more if they all the more have meant it if they have meant it all the more many marry here.

Four families make four sisters.

Four sisters make four more.

Four more make as much.

Four more make as much and more.

In this way ruin stares them in the face.

As funny she is as funny as that.

As that one.

Remembers nothing as much she remembers nothing as much she remembers nothing more she does not remember it at all.

Two more.

Fortunately she was fortunately, she was fortunate it is fortunate, very fortunate indeed.

Three times.

Abrupt is named, abruptly named it was abruptly named, it was as abruptly named, suddenly and not indignation.

Four and indignant. In this way a question in this way in question, very many say so.

Furnished, furniture.

Persuasion as persuasive.

Rejected by them.

As there and growing.

Three times three and not made forty.

Four times four and estimated.

Five times five for the only reason that is given.

Six times six as neglect.

They succeed in their way.

The first family to mention it.

The second family to mention it.

The first family and plainly felt to be in their way.

The second family originally favorably.

The second and third family have left.

The fourth family easily replaces friends.

Forty-four subtracted from forty-seven.

One companion.

Forty-four and forty-four.

Another companion.

Sixteen and ten, compared.

Five and a half makes it comparatively more so.

The next arrangement was made like this.

The first time that it was to be divided between them, in the place of it.

The second time all of it was prepared.

The third time was included.

Nothing further.

All the family was it a condition that they knew best.

Was it.

If a wife married a husband need they wish that they were to go there today.

If a sister had better do so need they decide quickly.

If a man and a man and more of it happened to have come again need any one be troubled.

If all of them go together and then one of them goes there and then all of them meet and then two of them stay is there any doubt about it.

The best of it all is this.

One of them has to be in a house in order to receive. Two of them have to be in the house in order to be ready. Three of them have to be in the house too.

Four of them are there from day to day. This is very necessary.

Who dances first.

Negroes.

Who dances next.

Negroes.

Who dances next after that.

Who dances next after that.

If a mother is pleased. Please.

If a brother is pleased. If you please.

If a sister is pleased if a sister is pleased does she follow follow me.

If a mother is pleased if a brother is pleased if a sister is pleased it does follow.

Smiling and that.

The first time it is foolish, the second time it is foolish. The second time it is foolish the first time the first time. It is foolish the first time. The third time as foolish the third time. Refuse the fourth time the fourth time more foolish the fourth time. More than in the way more than ever more than ever more so.

First second third fourth, a fourth a third a second and a first.

As soft a noise as that.

Suddenly as soft a noise as that.

As suddenly as soft a noise as that and as suddenly and as soft a noise as that and as suddenly as as soft a noise as that.

One follow one to follow one and money one and money and one to follow and one to follow and money to follow and money to follow and one to follow and one and money to follow and one to follow and money to follow and money to follow and one and money to follow. Follow also. To follow also. One and money to follow also and one to follow and money to follow and also and money and one to follow also money to follow also.

When there is when was she here at what time was she here.

Did she go out did she go out without my knowing about it, did she go out and did she go out.

Without our knowing about it do we know that she went out without our knowing about it. And when she went out and when she went out and if she went out, if she went out without our knowing about it. If she went out without our knowing about it. If she went out without our knowing about it when she went out without our knowing about it.

All pleases all teases all teases all pleases and placing pictures of bridges there.

Placing of pictures of bridges there.

The next time fortunately geraniums are bought. The next time fortunately the next time, the next time fortunately, fortunately the next time the geraniums are bought fortunately next time the geraniums are bought. And fortunately the next time fortunately the geraniums are bought the next time.

For nearly all the time for nearly all this time all this time for nearly all this time.

And nearly for nearly all this time.

Resisting resisting as much as that resisting it as much as that.

Admittedly.

As soft a noise admittedly.

How much of many.

Following as a habit.

First in the way at first in the way, at first way at first.

If he if he was nearly there and distributed it how many changes were there made at once were there to be made at once. Once or twice.

Following a serial.

In the first number he has to have he has to have it all.

A number of times.

In the first place as he has to have it as pleasantly as in the first place.

So much further.

In the first place he has to have it as pleasantly as in the first place.

So many more meant.

In the first place he has to have it so much more pleasantly than in the first place and so many more and as many more. Meant as much more.

In the first place he has to have it as pleasantly as in the first place and meant as much more.

In the first place he has to have it as pleasantly as in the first place.

The second number. Exchange exchanged to coming again.

Fairly exchanged to coming again. The second number fairly exchanged to coming again.

Now and then.

Have it have it very likely to have it, is very likely to have it he is very likely to have it all that must come in to it here and now.

Very likely to have it very likely to have it all of it must have come must very likely have come to have it must have come to have it, must like to have come to have it, here and now. Must very likely have come to have it he must very likely have had it.

The third number changes more than ever. As it has wandered away and he can say and he can say and he can say and he can say and he can say as nearly exactly as that.

The fourth number makes acquaintance. Acquaintances arrange it to arrange it to arrange it as acquaintances. To arrange it as acquaintances formerly to arrange it as acquaintances.

In the fifth number more changes. More changes in the fifth number.

The sixth number follows the fifth number and this is a synopsis.

If it is seen that rice if it is seen that rice resembles laughter if it is seen that rice and laughter joking comes repeatedly.

In wishes.

Joking comes repeatedly in wishes.

Rice and laughter and joking comes repeatedly in wishes.

To follow conquest.

Spaniards conquered Mexico and Spaniards conquered Peru too.

Spaniards conquered Mexico and Spaniards conquered Peru too.

After this fortunately.

Fortunately after this.

A reason for the differences that always exist.

If one place is mentioned and they know the streets in it, if one place is mentioned and they remember the streets in it, if one place is mentioned and they mention the streets that makes it as different as that.

If they mention a place and they mentioned the streets in it if they mention the streets in it it is as different as that.

This is a beginning and an introduction.

Reminded of East Oakland.

Reminded of East Oakland and is as different as that.

The next time all of them join they join as much so and as much so and as much so as that.

In this way every day and in every way in this way in every way and every day in this way is as much so.

What happened graphically.

Aroused again.

Nonchalance.

Two and three.

When he went.

Two and three.

Two and three when he went.

Two and three.

Much change from that also.

Two and three.

When he went.

Much change from that also.

Two and three when he went much change from that.

Much changed when he went also much changed when he went also two and three also much changed when he went.

Two and three.

She went there.

She went there and the difference that it made was this.

If five makes seven if five makes seven if five if five makes seven and counting.

She went there and the difference that it made was this.

Her father had known the son of the man who had been very well known.

If five makes seven the difference that it made was this.

Her father had known when he had known him he was the son of a man whom he had known who was known.

The difference that it made was this. When she went the difference that it made was this.

All doubt about sisters disappeared, no doubt about sisters

there was no doubt about the sisters there was no doubt that they were their sisters. In that way it was useful to them to them.

Undoubtedly scarcely not at all.

Following before and behind nearly. Nearly following.

Following fairly well.

When she when, when they when, when she and when they, when they so much as to tear, tear it up.

When she and when they, when they when she and when they and so and as much as if used as if they used it yearly.

She said that that this year being homesick she would return to the country but that next year but that next year in that case repeating it makes it sound longer. This makes reasons for it. This makes reasons for it.

She said that this year and a settling this year she said that this year and the reason for it this year she said this year there was a reason for it this year.

Have it today.

When he can say richly.

When he can say.

A mixture of that.

The first time they converse they know all about it.

The second time they converse they know all about it.

The third time they converse they know all about it.

The fourth time they converse they know all about it.

The fourth time they converse they know all about it.

Every one must remember that in making money no more excitement is necessary than in making this.

Every one must remember that in making money no more excitement is necessary than in making that.

Every one must know that in making money no more excitement is necessary.

Every one must know that in making money no excitement every one must know that in making money no more excitement is necessary at all.

So much so.

Every one must know that in making money as much so every one must know that in making money every one must know that in making money as much so no excitement is necessary as much so as at all. Every one must know that in making money no excitement is necessary at all.

Every one must know that in making money no excitement is necessary at all.

The next exchange comes readily.

Every one must know that in making money as much so no excitement is necessary at all.

The next time he wasn't wrong.

There were hardly any more examples than that.

It is quite sufficient to know that they occupied it is quite sufficient to know that it occupied, it is quite sufficient to know that it was occupied that it was occupied as much so as they said that it was as much occupied as they said that they were as much so as much occupied as they said.

A new serial and a return to resemblances.

He is a wonder and George Barney and a return to resemblance.

Just as soon just as soon as he said he was agreeable and pronounced so just as soon agreeably and as pronounced so, just as soon just as soon as he said he was agreeable agreeably and pronounced so, no circumstances no circumstances and change. It was readily changed and arranged. The next time more come. Out of the door. The next time agreeably as if it were changed, the next time as if it were changed and they come out of the door as if agreeably next time and as if it were to be changed.

Thanks for the message.

They have not heard from them. He has not heard from him. She has not heard from her. All these make resemblances attractive.

All these make resemblances as attractive as anything.

Formerly it was an occasion occasionally it was a return, in return. Formerly it was an occasion to return to it. Formerly occasionally it was returned for it. As an advantage and because more than enough occasionally more than enough.

Singularly settled as singularly as it can be.

The first serial to follow.

The second serial to follow.

The third serial to follow.

Fourteen and fifteen to follow sixteen sixteen to follow seventeen, eighteen and it was a deception.

Spend splendidly as it happens.

The next enough.

And declared for instance as it has to have to all of it. For more.

He said that they were politely careful.

She said that they were as politely careful.

They said politely that they were as careful as ever.

No one listens too much to them.

Come to it soon.

Come to it soon and say and to say and to say and to say come to it soon.

Come to it soon and to say come to it soon.

Next.

That is what he said.

Next.

That is what she said that she had heard that he had said.

The next time they make no difference either way. The next time they make no difference either way.

May he have the rest of his may he have the rest of his roses. Oh yes.

May he have the rest of his grapes. Oh yes.

May he have the rest of his grapes may he have the rest of the roses. Oh yes.

Beggars are in the country, there are beggars in the country she says that there are beggars in the country.

In the meantime there are various reasons why they are all why they all are there. In the meantime there are various reasons there are reasons there are various reasons why they are all there. The various reasons are these. He agrees he agrees that he feels he agrees that he feels it in this way he agrees that he feels it in this way in this case. He feels that he agrees that he feels it in this way in this case he feels that he agrees that in such a case he feels it in this way. This makes a collection. As collected together as collectedly or something. To be influenced by a little more, a little more influence, to be influenced a little

more and a little more and to be influenced by a little more, by
a little more to be influenced by it a little more, to be influenced
a little more by it.

The sad story of Italy and the Italians.

The sad story of the same. The same or the same. All the
same is it so. It is so all the same. It is so all the same and all the
same and it is so all the same. Next plenty of remarkable greeting. He greeted him with much pleasure. They greeted them
with much with as much pleasure.

Now then.

Now then.

Now then.

Now then.

Next to it.

He was near it.

If he can say three of them five of them if he can say five
of them but are five of them around, are there five of them
around.

If he can say three of them if he can say if not three of them
five of them are there five of them has he does he can he will
he, and will he if he says five of them if he says if not five of
them three of them, if he says three of them, if he says five of
them he has said, nothing has been decided as yet.

If he said five if he did say five of them or three of them, he
did say three of them, he preferred three of them, he preferred
five of them, he preferred three of them he did say three of
them, he said three of them he said if three of them.

Exactly as he said it.

To copy this too many times. Exactly as he said it and to
copy it too many times.

To notice arms and all that, to notice and arms and all that,
and notice arms. The result of that is this. This is the result of
that. This is the result of that that in looking at that and as
looking at that and not as looking on or at that or at that for
that not at all for that it was not at all what was needed for that.
Now and then.

In making a mistake in counting that is in counting four and no more, in making a mistake in counting, counting four.

In making a mistake in counting in counting two, in making a mistake in counting in not counting two and more.

In making a mistake in counting in making a mistake in not counting more.

In making a mistake in counting.

In making a mistake in counting in counting six in counting six and seven, in making a mistake in counting six and seven, in making a mistake in counting four, in making a mistake in counting two, in making a mistake in counting.

In making that mistake in counting.

In making that mistake in counting two more.

In making that mistake in counting two more in making that mistake in counting four.

In making that mistake in counting out loud in counting two more.

In making that mistake in counting out loud in counting four.

In making that mistake in counting out loud counting four out loud.

In making that mistake in counting out loud in counting out loud in counting more.

In making that mistake in counting seven and six.

In making that mistake in counting six.

In making that mistake in counting.

BIRTH AND MARRIAGE

(1924)

Barring yesterday she was born today. As she was born to-day it was nearly as carefully prepared as possible. Possibly she was born today and it was as carefully prepared as possible. It was as carefully prepared as possible and she was born today. So much for that.

He was born today and it was as carefully prepared as possible it was as carefully prepared as possible that he was born today. It was carefully prepared that he was born today. It was as carefully prepared as possible that he was born today.

She was born today it was as carefully prepared as possible and she was born today. It was as carefully prepared as possible that he was born today.

Next day. Next day she was born the next day, it was as carefully prepared as possible and she was born the next day. He was born the next day it was as carefully prepared as possible that he was born the next day. The next day and the next day, it was prepared as carefully as possible and she was born the next day and the next day and it was carefully prepared as possible that he was born the next day. The next day and the next day and the next day and it was as carefully prepared as possible and she was born the next day and it was as carefully prepared as possible that he was born the next day. And the next day and the next day and the next day.

From that day on that day it was as carefully prepared as possible.

If on that day and it was as carefully prepared as possible if she was born on that day it was as carefully prepared as possible if she was born on that day. If he was born and if he was born it was as carefully prepared as possible if he was born and if he was born on that day. And so forth.

For him for her, for for it. For it for her for her for him for it.

If for her if for her and if for him if for it, if he was born

if for him if she was born if for her if she was born for it if
he was born for it, if he was born if she was born if for if for it,
if she was born if for it if he was born if for it. If for it if he
was born for it, if for it if she was born for it, if she was born
if for it if he was born if for it, if he was born if she was born
if for it if she was born for it. If she was born if he was born
if for it if he was born for it.

As many as as many as that, as many as that as many. If as
many if as many as that. As coming gradually. So much and as
might might be.

As much a reason. It was as much a reason for it it was as
much a reason for it as it was as it ever was it was as much a
reason for it as it ever was.

It was as much a reason for it it was as much a reason for it
as it ever was. And more nearly the same. It was as much a
reason for it as it ever was and more nearly the same. It was
as much a reason for it as it ever was and more nearly the same.

Come to having been born and there was nearly as much
reason for it and more nearly and as nearly and nearly the same.
There was as much reason for it and more nearly the same.

Continuing and continuing and as it and as he was and as
he is and continuing and more nearly the same and as he was
born and as he is born and continuing and more nearly the same.
And more nearly the same and continuing and she is and as she
is and as she is born and continuing and more nearly the same
and continuing and she is and as she is and is born and continuing
and more nearly the same and continuing and more nearly the
same.

Not as it was it was not as it was it was not as it was when
as it was it was more it was more so as it was. As it was and so
as it was it was as it was so.

Having been born and so and so forth. Having been born
so and so. He having been born so and so and so forth and she
having been born so and so.

After that perhaps sufficiently, after perhaps as sufficient
after that perhaps as sufficiently and he was perhaps after that
sufficiently and preparations were perhaps after that sufficiently
perhaps after there were perhaps sufficient preparations made.

Sufficient preparations were made for him. Sufficient preparation was made for her. Not altogether. It comes to that not altogether. Not altogether and not altogether. At first as he came
first, at first as she came first, at first as she came first at first
as he came first.

He came first. At first he came first.

She came first. At first she came first. In this way he was
indispensable.

In this way he was indispensable he came first. At first he
came first. At first she came first, at first he came first and it
was indispensable that he came first. At first he came first at
first she came first.

And then to receive. How many can come to count three.
No one. How many can come to count one. And one. How
many can come to count two. And two. How many can come
to count five and five. How many can come to count at first.
At first how many can come to count at first.

She was born first at first. He was born first at first.

The next time there was this as an instance. For instance he
was born first at first. For instance she was born first at first.

In the next place as in the next place, in the next place more
and more and more and more in the next place. And for instance.

When the occasion when for the occasion not occasionally
and refusal, not refusal and occasionally not occasionally not
refusal occasionally, when they had met when had they met,
when had they met when they had met.

As soon as that. As soon as that they had met as soon as
that, she had met as soon as that he had met as soon as that they
had as soon as that they had met as soon as that he had met as
soon as that she had she had met she had met as soon as that.

In that and there lay in that in their way it had lain in that
way it had lain in their way it had lain as they may it had lain
as they may may they as it lay may she as it lay may he as it
lay as it lay may he as it lay may she as it lay may she as it lay
may she as it lay may he as it lay may he yesterday as it lay
may she today as it lay may he today as it lay may she yesterday as it lay may she yesterday as it lay and may it lay has it
lain in this way has it lain in their way in this way does it lay

in this way does it lay in their way does it lay in this way does
it lay in their way. Yesterday in this way, and this way and in
this way and in this way and today and in this way and as this
way, and as this way and this way, anyway, anyway this way,
in this way lain in this way lain in this way lain in their way in
this way, in this way and in this way and lain in their way in
this way.

To make and make, to make as much as to make, accepted,
to make as to make, accepted, to make and as to make and accepted.

When the ring around the rosy when and ring, when the
ring around the rosy and when and ring. When the ring around
the rosy and make and accepted, when the ring and when
around and when the rosy and when and make and when and
accepted and when the ring around the rosy and when and accepted. For instance not two more for instance not two more
and when and make and accepted and when and not two more.
When the ring around the rosy and when and make and accepted and not two and not two more.

The results, the results the results three results four results
two results or results or resulted it resulted in this.

Formerly as they had formerly as she had formerly as he
had had come again and again and in arrangement. Marriage by
arrangement, arrange to marry. As arranged and as married.
This was not the beginning, this was not only centrally but
serviceably settled. For this reason no fairly not at all, for this
reason not fairly not at all and each one satisfied to say so. Not
as birth and cunning.

To proceed to begin.

How do you do this evening. Very well I thank you. How
do you do this morning. Very well I thank you and you. Very
well I thank you and how do you do this afternoon. Very well
I thank you and you. Very well I thank you. Birth and marriage
and needs to needs to. Birth and marriage and needs to.

The next time that it was sent the next time that it was sent
the next time was it sent was it sent there.

In as many places. In as many places as that. Not wishing not as wishing remembering not as wishing and remembering and not as wishing.

Considerable birth and considerable birth. As birth as birthday, considerable birth as considerable birth. It is as considerable as at birth.

In the first place.

In the first place as she was born in the first place. In the first place as he was born in the first place. As he was born in the first place. As she was born as they were born, in the first place as they were born. How do you do.

In the first place the necessary service, serve her first. In the first place and the necessary service and to serve him first. Serve them at first, they serve them at first and at first, and at first they serve them. They serve them themselves. And as much and as much as that. Nearly necessary it is nearly necessary it is as nearly necessary it is more nearly necessary, it is more nearly and more nearly it is as necessary as necessary, it is very nearly as necessary, it is very nearly so. They were born very nearly so. They were born and very nearly so.

The first to admit the first to admit the first to be admitted, admitted is it admitted is it admitted as more and more so. And at first so and nearly so and nearly so and more so and at first, and so at first. They were born at first. First they were born. First at first, he was born first at first. She was born and born first and at first. Very nearly and not very nearly. Completely, for instance. The next time as admiration.

Seriously say as much.

If the one if the one and one if the one and one and two if the one and one and two, if two if two and one and one, commence again to delight.

Commence again seriously to delight.

Commencing again seriously to delight, delightful, commencing again seriously delightful to delight, to delight commencing again to delight delightful seriously to delight. To delight commencing again to delight commencing again delightful, commencing again to delight, commencing again delightful.

Delightfully commencing again and delight.

One who is an instance of finding it out.

One who is an instance of finding it out.

How about it.

One who is an instance of finding it out and finding it out and how about it.

One who is an instance of finding it out. How about it and finding it out and how about it.

They made it, made, too, and two, make they made two and two, they made it they made it too. They made it, too and they made it. It is at this time. It is at this time and it is and it is at this time and it is at this time.

Ordinarily, this comes to have places and places and ordinarily and this comes to have places and places.

Birth and marriage yesterday.

The first time and recital the first time, the first time and the recital the first time. The first time the recital has has it and has it and the recital, has it the recital and so much recitation. So much recitation and louder. Recitation as so much louder and recitation and recitation, so much louder. If this could be the reason that the direction, direction as directed if this could be the reason for more direction, direction and as directed for instance. There was this way further.

What is it.

Two more two more any day two more two more two more two more any day.

Two more went to more.

Birth and marriage yesterday and so forth.

Answer questions.

In an answer as much as an answer in answer it was in answer that they had to do it. It was as their answer that they did it. Nobody questioned yes and nobody questioned and yes and nobody had questioned and nobody had questioned and yes.

More easily

When when is it, when was it, when is it to be.

When is it.

Not nearly as much so as that.

She as she compared, to compare, and not obliged to do so.

He and she and she and he and not obliged to do so.

As today as two today and as two and as two today. Change it to change it.

If and this is the same when and as this is the same where and where this is the same why and why and willing to be so.

If names are needed if names are more needed more and more needed and needed.

One went on to say so. He went on to say so.

While it was while it was was it once in a while.

While it was it was while it was and for this and as this and this is what is the matter.

Birth and marriage makes noises, makes noises as it were, makes noises as it were, makes noises and as it was and as it was birth and marriage.

Birth so much. Marriage so much, birth and marriage so much. Birth and marriage and so much.

He said, he said, he said, said it, he said he said it, he said it was said. She as much as said it. She said it as much as he said it.

Being born today. He said it as much as he said it. He said it just as much, he said it just as much and he said it as much as much as he said it and being born today that way in that way fairly well. The next thing to do and was it because of this the next thing to do was the decision as to older and younger. After that there was the decision as to older and younger. She said that there was to be a decision as to older and younger. When there was a decision as to older and younger the next thing to do was to do that.

The next thing to do was to do that the next thing to do was to do that the decision the next thing to do was to do that. That was the decision.

The happiness of the bride. Birth and marriage or the happiness of the bride. Or not enough. The happiness of the bride or not enough or the happiness of the bride. Birth and marriage or the happiness of the bride.

When they thought when they had thought when he had thought, though it was as often as every time that it was changed, changing makes it so easy to have it born, it is born he is born she is born, she was born he was born and so much more, to begin easily.

To begin easily is what makes conversation so soon. Conversation so soon and to begin easily.

Two, three, three, two, one two, two one, one two three, three two, one two three three too, three two three two one two one two three. This is the way to count. Three more can make almost a million. This was not only estimated.

To suppose and not remember, said so to suppose said so and not remembered said so to suppose said so to suppose and not remembered said so not remembered said so to suppose so.

He said, I remember very well, I cannot say that I do remember it well, I say I do remember it very well, I remember it very well.

She said, I do remember it very well I say I do remember it very well I can say I do remember it very well, I say that I can say that I can that I can and that I do remember it very well.

More than all of it.

He can say he can say that he can say that. She can say that and she can say that.

Particularly as it is to be there.

Birth and marriage for instance.

If mounting if amounting if it is amounting to that birth and marriage for instance if it is amounting to that.

For nearly as much so.

Beginning, met as can decide beside it. As can decide beside it, met as can decide beside it.

When Amy S. Henry was born in the usual way it was all ready and already and already it was all ready everything was already in the usual way. The only thing that was perhaps unusual was the presence of one may say of nearly all of them individually. If we may say so the presence of every one individually. In this way birth at birth in this way at her birth in this way at her birth and in this way and at her birth. She was born to stay, staying in that way.

Every one who was there no one was present except those needed as is usual.

How can anything be introduced.

There can be no conversation when there is no noon. At noon.

Individually and usage, used used for this purpose only and very neatly. So much so that the pleasure, the pleasure of losing, the pleasure of losing who had the pleasure of losing it. Neither one of them.

The next time in a way if two are present one in one place and the other in the other place any reason which is given is given by every one as they say.

Who decides. Playfully.

It was very pleasant to feel that really when it had happened as it is often said when it had really happened as it is often said it was very pleasant to feel that it had really happened as it is often said.

Birth and marriage separately. Birth first and then after this then after this then after this birth then after this born after this and birth and born after this and born and after this.

Birth and born and after this.

The next occasion for reaching, reaching, and as the next occasion and reaching, to reach. To reach an occasion to reach it and occasion to reach it.

Birth not birthday, born not as born. Birth and birthday born and born.

If if it, if it is, if it is as if it is as appropriate, if it is as appropriate as if it is appropriately appropriately if it is birth and marriage if it is, birth and marriage if it is. If it is birth and marriage if it is.

Accompaniment. Who is ashamed of an accompaniment.

I am.

Who is ashamed of an accompaniment. She knows that it is not an accompaniment.

Who is ashamed of an accompaniment.

Is it an accompaniment.

Is it an accompaniment, who is ashamed of an accompaniment who is ashamed if it is an accompaniment.

She is not ashamed and it is not an accompaniment.

Nearly said so.

An instance of this is preparation. An instance of this to prepare to prepare it.

If to be if it is to be said to be if it is said to be or if it is to be said to be, to be said to be so.

Funnily fed so.

The first born.

Who was born first.

He was born first.

And as funnily and funnily so it was funnily so.

When was she born.

She was born on the thirtieth of April just before the first of May. She was born before the first of May she was born on the thirtieth of April just before the first of May.

Can one really mean what one says.

In exchange.

As an exchange.

To exchange.

An exchange.

If he if he if he does say so. If he does say so and so and so. If he does say so. If he does say so.

If she does say so, she says so, she says so if she does say so.

Birth and marriage makes society. Birth and marriage makes society for them.

She is as if to say, she is as if to say she is as if to say, if as if to say.

Remembering cautiously.

Counting no longer counts.

They leave to leave, two to leave, and to leave too.

Nearly to to nearly to nearly have to have it to nearly have to have it as nearly as as nearly as it is.

The next twenty more.

And the next twenty more.

She feeling as she does about it.

Success.

What is success.

Success is the result achieved when nobody answers.

Success is the result achieved.

Fairly well fairly well shown to be, it is fairly well shown to be it is shown to be it is fairly well shown to be.

Completely fairly well, fairly well shown to be fairly well.

Birth and marriage yesterday. Yesterday so many reasons, yesterday. Fairly well shown to be.

Birth and marriage fairly well shown to be yesterday fairly well shown to be fairly well shown to be so many reasons fairly well shown to be fairly well shown to be birth and marriage.

Birth and marriage.

Birth first, marriage first. Marriage first, birth first. Birth and marriage first. Fairly well shown to be birth and marriage first, fairly well shown to be many reasons fairly well shown to be birth and marriage fairly well shown to be, birth and marriage.

Birth and marriage.

Birth first.

Marriage first.

Birth and marriage first.

The difference in character there is this difference in their character.

They cannot be deceived.

Birth and marriage splendidly.

You are happy and smiling and everything is rosy and you have no worries and no excitements. In spite of everything you accommodate yourself easily to the arrangements necessary to the spending of what you have. Clearly.

Do not be surprised if in easily repeating what has been already said and done there are indications of returning to accomplish what has been done already.

More than most.

If birth is succeeded by marriage if marriage is succeeded by birth, birth and marriage fairly nearly there. Birth and marriage fairly nearly there.

Not a little not a little not so much, not a little and not so much.

As good as they are beautiful.

When he was born and they said so when was he born and they said so, when was she born and they said so.

When he was born and they said so when was he born and they said so.

After that and linen.

When was she born and they said so and after that and then linen.

When she was born and they said so and after that and then linen.

In as used.

Mostly yes and mostly no.

No more.

Having heard it.

Having heard it too.

Having had it.

As having had it.

If he was born if he was born as he was born today as he was born today waiting every day.

Waiting every day.

As she was born today as she was born today as she was born today.

As she was born as he was born as he was born as she was born.

Not a little.

Not so much.

As he was born and as he was and as she was born and as she was.

All of all of all of all of all of all of it.

All of it and all of it and all of it all of it. So much so.

The next arrangement is one in which excitement presses.

And the next arrangement is one in which and the next arrangement is one in which and the next arrangement orderly.

When it comes oftener, how often.

When it comes oftener.

The next question.

When it comes oftener.

The next question when it comes oftener.

How often when it comes oftener the next question when it comes oftener. The next question when it comes oftener.

She was fond of being the only daughter.

The next question when it comes oftener.

When it comes oftener.

She was fond of being the only daughter the next question when it comes oftener.

Part two for more.

Part two for more nearly.

Part two for more nearly she was fond of being an only daughter.

The next question for that is this.

She was fond too, part two for more nearly she was fond too of being an only daughter and so forth.

Part two and for more nearly for more. Part two and for more and nearly for more.

She was fond of being an only daughter part two and for more.

The next time an only daughter and an only son. The next time one was younger. The next time part two and for more and nearly and being the only daughter. The next time part two and for more and nearly and mistaken and for more and part two and nearly. The next time and an only daughter and an only son.

If an only daughter and an only son are they mistaken. Yes because he was one of seven and she was one of two.

Was a marriage nearly all was all of it nearly a marriage too was a marriage too nearly all, nearly all and was a marriage nearly all. Yes nearly all. All in all. So much so.

Was a marriage nearly all so much so all in all so much so, nearly so much so. So much so to come too.

Next wedding the next wedding nearly so much so nearly all so much so, nearly all nearly all so much so. The next wedding nearly all so much so.

For instance why do they two thirds do they, why do they do why two thirds do they, do they two thirds do they. The next time so much so nearly so much as nearly all, all in all so much so.

Birth and marriage makes yesterday fairly well, fairly well yesterday, so much so fairly well yesterday nearly all yesterday fairly well nearly all so much so, all in all nearly all fairly well yesterday so much so.

Further than that yes further than that no, further than that yes further than that no.

Further than that.

Further than that yes.

The next time they are they ate there. The next time that they ate, ate.

The next time that they ate that the next time that they ate.

He and she and expressly.

He and she and expressly.

He she and expressly.

The next thing makes a residence. A residence has to have oak leaves or for it. The next thing has to have have had it. The next thing has to have have had it.

The next thing for this to be obliging. The next thing for this to be obliging for this to be obliging.

Next to marrying not to next to marrying as that. Birth and marriage and say so to say so, birth and marriage to say so. To say so birth and marriage to say so.

Birth and marriage as being arranged. This is so.

If by reorganization if by reorganization he meant in the course of organization rapidly for this readily. If she in the course of their return returned it as particularly as for the transport of persons and baggage if they meant to intercept the return of the arrangement as they had been prepared as if they had been prepared to do so, to do so.

Now then continuance makes yesterday fortunately for for them. Fortunately for for them. Fortunately for them for them. Fortunately for them. As fortunately for them. They fortunately for them for them fortunately for them fortunately. In this case in that case in case of fortunately for them this fortunately for them, this for them, this for them fortunately for them this fortunately for them for this fortunately for this for them, for them, for this, fortunately for this fortunately.

Fortunately makes more than fortunately makes more then makes more then fortunately makes more then.

She had it in her to have inside her she had it in her she had it in her to have inside her she had it in her to have it inside her the three of it as much, reference to it, in preference to it, in

order to do it in order for it, in the rest for it, in resting for it
she had it in her to have it inside her she had it in her to have
it inside in her and then as it is said and then as it is as it is said
and then as it is and then as it is said and then as it is as it is said
as it is as it is as it is said, it is as it is as it is said. He too makes no
one see suddenly as much, he too as much he too as much more
and so forth so that in that case and not at all as so much as as
much as as much as it is it is as much as it is so much as much as
much more also.

Now and then.

She said thank you very much. You are welcome. She said
you are welcome. She said thank you very much and she said
you are very welcome.

Now secretly starting.

Now secretly starting not starting to start. Not secretly starting not secretly starting to start, not secretly starting not at all
secretly not at all starting to start. Not at all and not at all.

Begin as not singing so, sing song, or sing song so.

Birth and marriage continuously.

Let us neglect nothing.

Birth and marriage is one way of birth and marriage is one
way of birth and marriage is one way of birth and marriage and
almost so.

Birth and marriage connectedly.

Birth and marriage.

If you make it so if you make birth and marriage so if as
you make birth and marriage if you make birth and marriage
so as birth and marriage so.

Let it, let us.

In the beginning in the beginning having had having had, in
the beginning in the beginning, having had and having had and
having had in the beginning let us in the beginning let us as let
us in the beginning in the beginning as let us.

Can you see to believe two believe can you see two believe
can you see two believe.

Formerly as fact look a fact in the face.

Look a fact in the face formerly as fact.

Formerly as fact.

Look a fact in the face.

Formerly as fact.

The next pleasure.

The next pleasure is the next pleasure. The next pleasure is the next pleasure too. Two and two. The next pleasure is the next pleasure too, two and two. Two and two the next pleasure is the next pleasure, two and two. The next pleasure is the next pleasure, two and two, the next pleasure is the next pleasure is the next pleasure. The next pleasure is the next pleasure too. They meant to say they meant to say that the next pleasure they meant to say too that the next pleasure is the next pleasure too, they meant to say that the next pleasure is the next pleasure too.

He felt as well as that. If fortunately if fortunately if fortunately to say so if to say so fortunately to say so if to say so if to say it fortunately to say so. Fortunately to say so.

Not at all started.

Birth and marriage makes at most birth and marriage makes at most, birth and marriage makes at most. At most.

Birth and marriage makes at most. What is the difference between six and one at once.

Birth and marriage makes at most, at most, birth and marriage makes at most, at most. Birth and marriage makes at most.

For this and for this.

And for this for this.

River.

Changes.

And for this for this.

For this and for this.

River

Changes.

Birth and marriage makes it most.

Nearly has.

It nearly has.

It has nearly.

It has nearly been so.

Also.

It has nearly been so.

As it has nearly been so.

Birth and marriage and was he birth and marriage and was he careful birth and marriage and was he careful and birth and marriage and was he careful of birth and marriage carefully and careful of birth and marriage and was he carefully. She must she must, one and one, she must and she must, one and one, one and one she must she must one and one.

The next effect is four the next effect or to do so, and to do so. The next effect.

And to do so makes a gift. Gifted.

And to do so makes a gift and to do so.

And to do so makes a gift, gifted and to do so, gifted makes a gift and to do so.

One and one, see one and one, one and one see see one and one, see one and one, one and one see.

And to do so makes and to do so, one and one, see, one and one, see, gifted, makes it to do so.

One and one see makes it to do so, gifted, one and one, see makes it do so, makes it do so, one and one, see.

When he had shown her what he had done when he was and to do so, when he had shown her one and one, and when to do so, when had he when had he, when to do so, when he had shown her one and one, see, when to do so.

When she had and when she had and when to do so, one and one and see and she and when and when to do so and gifts and when to do so and one and one and see and gifted and see and when to do so and one and one and see and when to do so and one and one and see.

The next time he was the next time he was the next time he was as seen so much. Favorably.

The next time as she was favorably and so much settled and so much favorably and so much as much have it as much.

Birth and marriage is the occasion birth and marriage is the occasion which has been known and known.

Birth and marriage is the occasion which has been intended to be which has been known and known.

Birth and marriage and as frequently and as frequently known and know, birth and marriage as frequently known.

Birth and marriage one two three four and one above, birth and marriage and more. More as birth and marriage.

More as birth and marriage conditionally.

Birth and marriage fully as fully known to be as fully as that. Birth and marriage fully known to be as fully known to be known and known as that.

As easily as explained.

Birth and marriage and green trees, and as green trees. Birth and marriage and as green trees and as green trees, birth and marriage green trees green fields and green trees, and green trees. Birth and marriage and green trees.

Birth and marriage and so so. Count them. One two three four five six seven eight nine ten eleven twelve. Not describable because it would take it take it it would not take it away, not describable because they do not absolutely make it do. Describe twelve like that unalike, irregular, following as thin, as if, as placed, as well, forty make four and has nothing to do with it. Five sixty-eight seven eleven 568711 and written so and written slowly. Begin soft, begin as soft as that she began to be as soft as that he began. He began to begin to begin he began he began to begin to be as soft as that. She began to begin to begin she began she began she was begun as soft as that. She was begun she had begun she began she did begin she did begin she began and began as soft as that. How soft is that. Birth and marriage together as soft as that. Situated. As soft as that situated.

He began as soft as that situated, she began she was begun as soft as that situated. Here in sight.

Birth and marriage made yesterday and told nicely. Leave birth and marriage made yesterday and told nicely.

Birth and marriage, birth and marriage together and made yesterday and told nicely birth and marriage and told nicely and made yesterday, birth and marriage and made yesterday and told nicely and made yesterday and told nicely and birth and marriage and made yesterday. Birth and marriage and told nicely and made yesterday and told nicely and made yesterday and made yesterday and told nicely and birth and marriage and told nicely and birth and marriage and made yesterday.

And a list. A list of names a list of names a list of names and nearly a list of names and nearly a list of names and told nicely and made yesterday and nearly and a list of names and made yesterday and nearly and a list of names and nearly and nearly a list. And nearly a list.

What is there to see there, what is there to see three and a Saturday what is there to see three to see there to seat there what is there to see there what is there to see what is there to see to sit there and there to sit three and three to seat three and there. That makes six. Six more make twelve what is there to see twelve as green as to see to see twelve as green as three and twelve to sit there to sit there and what is there to see what is there to see to sit there to seat there, to seat three there. Next. She was married yesterday birth and marriage yesterday to sit there birth and marriage yesterday to sit there nicely told to sit birth and marriage yesterday, birth and marriage yesterday to sit there yesterday nicely told to birth and marriage to sit there yesterday. This is all of today anyway not only yesterday.

I like it best when it goes up in front all the way as all the way I like it best when it is right away when it cannot be stopped in any way I like it best when I can see it that way I like it best when there is no way, I like it best.

It is a highly desirable offer offer of itself.

I like it best that way, I like it best in that way why do they say lady bird lady bird fly away why do they say come into my parlor said the spider to the fly, butterfly why do they say lady bird lady bird fly away home your house is on fire your children are burning why do they say will you come into my parlor said the spider to the fly, butterfly.

I like it best when it goes up and when it goes up I like it best when it goes along I like it best when it goes up I like it best when as it goes along all of it goes along I like it best when all of it goes along, I like it best when it goes up and nobody goes up, I like it best when nobody goes up, I like it best when it goes up and nobody goes up.

Poplars are very adaptable they always act as if the wind had always had been from that direction.

Birth and marriage makes makes it.

An incident in birth and marriage as incident as an incident in birth and marriage. An incident in birth and marriage is this. If four more were four more that would make twenty-eight at once, if four more were four more and it would make twenty-eight at once supposing that there were twenty-eight at once and four more were four more and four more and there were twenty-eight at once it would be best that they had best see they had best seen that they had been seen and now not as it could. Again if four more and twenty-eight at once if twenty-eight at once, four more and twenty-eight at once if four more, twenty-eight at once would would it have been would if we all know better and so we are sweet. Explained again.

Now and then now and then when they carry all now and then, carry long carry along carry long, now and then.

Birth and marriage and authority. Birth and marriage and authority instinctively.

Now then. She was born, he was born he was born. As she was born, he was born. Birth and marriage and authority. As he was born and he was born. As he was born and authority. Follow today. Next time to keep it dry. Next time to keep it dry and dear and clear. The story is this, he was commonly said to be sold. She was commonly said to be told, she was commonly said to be told he was commonly said to be sold. What is selling for. Selling is formerly used as an indication of repetition and so easily quoted. She was commonly told and what is this an indication of it is an indication of what is so easily meant. Meant today. He was born and she was born, born so. He was born and she was born he was born and she was born so. The story is this as an instance of wishes she is an instance of and fairly and he was also aimed at that. The story of it is this for instance if bells if bells amuse any one and if bells amuse any one and if bells amuse any one. The next time all of them remain there and tell it to them.

Now and then a story of bought her, brought her, sought her. Now and then a story of caught her. He caught her out and this is known as an expression.

So so so so so soon so so, so so so soon and eating at noon. At noon so so so so so so so so at noon so soon so soon so so.

And as for that and as for that, and as for that. A cloud and

as for that. It is considerably in the way of that the description
is of the places that before as if they were not to be appreciated.
Now we appreciate them we make them have it to be as said and
said so. So so, so soon, everybody so so so soon. It was a place as
was said.

Have, have permanently, have permanently as to have as to
have here, have permanently, have permanently as to have, permanently as if for the experience of that, have as to have, hear
it again had he. Hear it again had she, hear it again had he had
she, a multiplication of what we saw where. Where did we see
it.

This is what he said. He said that when he saw yellow and
blue blow and then when he saw yellow and blue blow, when
he saw yellow and blue blow, when he saw yellow and blue
blow he was satisfied.

If she said it was made up by them if he said it was made up
so that if as pleasantly as it appeared it made several and no mistakes not mistaken it was not mistaken to compare it. Consider it
as united, supposing they spoke in advertising of reengagement
would that mean that it was to be arranged that in changing
fortunately the number of places was unlimited and they had
nothing further to withdraw. In stating this they make no mistake. Imitation is the following at the same time as before. Imitate a succession of reasonable practices, imitate having attributed
more to them than ever, imitate familiar arrangements, imitate
altogether. In this way he followed and in this way he followed
and in this he followed.

Not merely a say so. This is what it looked like. Every day
it looked like this. The next day in any way not in any way the
next day was as nearly the next day as the day before and this
is what it looked like it looked like this in that way in the way
it was on the way. On the way stopping as often as not, stopping
as often stopping as often as not to see not looking at it because
it is as frequently mentioned before. Before now, as before now
reminding if not different reminding if not different for instance
birth and marriage before now if not different, birth and marriage for instance if before now if not different, birth and marriage has it as it as it has to be nearly before the resemblance to

the that reminds that that is to remind for instance to be reminded and so so, and so and so and so as it and as it is really it
is mingled with spoons and seasons and earlier and fitfully and
romantic and more so and extended. I did not mean to use the
name of a man.

Having birth and marriage moderately prefixed now. Having
it moderately prefixed now. Established states, in this way in
looking again no one need not, not any one need not any one
needed not as any one needed not to be and now changing
kneeded. The bread is very good. Describe nothing better.

Once again having it all in that way surely more.

Now not now not now not and not now. For instance would
it be better to have to see certainly to have to see what to see.
What to see, is it the same as and to see is it as nearly this as found
out there all separated by it so that as in passing it not in passing it forward as far back. Not neglected as lighter, to light, too
light, not neglected as lighter, have to see it again.

Birth and marriage makes money and a mountain and scenery
and places and greens and poplars and roofs and how do you do,
how do you do all the time not as begun but more and more and
longer. She was longer he was longer as long as that. Birth and
marriage radically. To begin again seeing and saying that all
the same.

A landscape formed by the surroundings and suitably fea-
tured, the landscape features are these, trees placed fortunately
for meadows and places, hills placed favorably and even mountains, mountains placed as favorably and even hills, trees placed
favorably and always as the same. The next time for meadows
and water and places. The next time as evenly.

Landscape interests us as we have said, for as we have said,
for as we have said, landscape interests us as we have said.

Landscape interests us as we have said, for as we have said
landscape as we have said interests us as we have said.

Birth and marriage and she gave me one and I gave her one I
gave her the one that had sleeves and pockets and she gave me
the one that was soft.

When you see one behind the other you attach one to the
other. Sometimes one is attached to the other as the one having

been attached by itself and often the one and the other by itself. This was the day that grass was red as red as that and glass was the same was the same as that and please to and pleased for and pleased five now. All of it makes a place for it.

Who says that.

I do.

Who says all that.

I do.

Who says it all.

I do.

Who says it.

I do.

Who says so.

Now come to see me by this I mean when you look down and see an eye is it as nearly pleasant as it is. More nearly pleasant as it is. More nearly pleasant as it is.

In the first place birth and marriage has meant this to me. It has meant that as if that as if that is as if it is as if it was all prepared, it was as if it had all been prepared and it was by order and by investigation. By order and investigation and next by order and investigation and next by order and investigation. In this way all followed the first.

Why do directions satisfy, they satisfy because as they follow as they do follow because as they do follow, follow it. This makes no preparation necessary at all. Birth and marriage follows me. Dear old tender here we come right back where we started from and so and so much. Again.

Magnificent and say so magnificent and said so and nobody angry. The change came about in this way, always fastening the band to the tree in such a way that the tree passed by any one one might have it as a banner or there. To sound as much so and no one literally no one to comfort. There is no one to be comforted. Literally and no one to be comforted. Moreover he wishes, wishes it. We all allow everything, an allowance.

Birth and marriage makes dates carry carry all birth and marriage and it it were set afire would they be careful that it did not burn at all. In saying so and saying and Mont Blanc. Not to be introduced. No one uses and uses and uses and no one uses and so and uses. She was nearly not to be expected. The explanation of that is this. Birth and marriage makes so much delicious. Occasionally as principally fastened and principally fastened as fastened together. Birth and marriage notable notably, birth and marriage when it is collected, recollected. And in no way that kind and as variety. Birth and marriage makes so much in english. So much so. We know it as a name.

I see scenery as to be as to be and as to see, as to see seen safer, seen safer so as it has fairly nearly for exacted. I have never seen a prettier cross or one so high. Fairly nearer fewer and the next higher as if collected for it recollected by it, recollected as it. As it is seen so seen so and birth and marriage mentioned yesterday as to say, as to say today, as to say today for we saw it yesterday. Birth and marriage yesterday and to say and to say birth and marriage and to say and seen to say, to say seen to say. I have never seen as pretty a cross I have never seen as pretty a cross as that or as frequently. Birth and marriage to say birth and marriage to say birth and marriage.

Birth and marriage makes mine a continuation of a sonatina followed by another.

A DIARY

(1927)

Helen bought a chicken to be boiled. If not in time veal. In time.

Eyes might.

Find only letters.

Thought.

If it is not a day when bear a bear is to bear.

In the early morning thought of other people's impoliteness.

Include a narrative.

A narrative cannot be when in when is heard. Because a narrative to get impatient when anybody tells a story this means a story of others this means a story and therefore a narrative and therefore.

One thing all.

A narrative story italics inundation replace tickets into all find it not a past time past time to insult to insult two.

Why does a narrative replace a diary. Because it does not.

One day

One day day before yesterday.

We went to I went to the garage and came back and made a detour and saw to it. That in passing by they having gone for the first time I heard three days after of his habit of traveling with a bible.

Today.

Not to yield to the temptation today of adding today. I did. I am I can. I can depend depend upon idolatry of spoons and water.

Why could she sleep. Because she can.

Friday.

There is a difference between omitting and there is a difference between adding.

Saturday. Today.

They went to the place that was not yet ready for them. But it was.

Yesterday today.

Helen is to buy a roast of pork and she is also to be ready to relate just what happened.

We went to see the house that was built and we found it not filled but easily able to contain more contain more contained Jenny Helen William Mildred and Pictus. They were not there. Jenny and William are coming to be one having been one having been not coming to be welcome welcome Louise.

John Johnny John Johnny we are sorry sorry John Johnny Johnny John John John so.

Josephine Josephine Josephine we are so sorry Josephine Josephine Josephine so.

George George George George George George we are so sorry George George we are so sorry George so.

That is on one account.

Naturally they are if they are asked naturally they are, if they are asked.

Helen is very pleased with Bravig and wonders why it is not he rather than Virgil who is asked to stay.

When widow's wishes when widow's wishes with them they must be read aloud.

When with windows undeniably when can it have it might it coming to be near it.

Tuesday. Every Tuesday and on some other day Janet receives visitors every Tuesday and on some other day. This is not only requited but is an ancient custom. Ancient and custom. Ancient when Oakland Oakland Oakland changed Oakland to Meadowsville.

Tuesday is still today.

Did not see Reagan yesterday.

A diary is not a line a day book.

Helen bought a chicken again twice.

It was necessary that it should be finished when she was not to be willing to be of assistance and timely timely does not mean at once but help help it.

And a little thing before them.

There is a question whether birds little ones before or flowers let it be rain are the most attractive.

Three days added together.

Choura came and come and Janet and came and Camelia if it was changed never having wished to leave the home. Also the difference between Nancy and new and the last name first and after all churches and little of with white white like and the day before Virgil was asked and the day before Virgil was asked and admit.

Simply told events.

Every day Miss Buckingham that Miss Buckingham comes she has something to tell of Gabrielle she has also something to say of a land inland which is an island. She is not desirous of leaving anything to it more to it more.

A diary of how I told everybody what is the problem of description what is the problem of accounting what is the problem that I have in mind. I have the problem of mind of inclosure of rubicund of last of invite and by nearly it was like it when it was animated.

A diary of later events.

There is no difference between seventeenth eighteenth nineteenth and twentieth.

Wrote a great many sketches.

She asked me not to introduce surprises nor leavings nor annoyances and I did not but it seems so. She also asked me if I would not like to receive for them a great deal of money and I agreed, I certainly would find it to be a very great pleasure to be abundantly paid. She and this was another case told me I should not give anything away for nothing and I would very much like not to do so. She again this was not by this one also said that it would be better to get back what I had loaned. I find that I do not really mind very much if I do not.

Helen has been supplied with little pieces of a wild animal wild and therefore delicious. It will be a very pleasant change if it were not necessary to go and celebrate with a friend at the end of the week who is very well content with an achievement. Anything which is impossible to refuse is accepted.

We walked today to tell some one that we had done so and we did not. This was because it was unpleasant unpleasantly and unpleasantly said. After all they might have been left to them.

Yesterday evening Bravig and John were here. They will be here again.

Several times other people have been here. There is a difference of opinion as to the desirability of their being here.

I have concluded that as a wife is a cow is perfect. As a wife is perfect as a cow is perfect as a wife has a cow is perfect it is to be reprinted.

Today we had plenty of advantages. She was not satisfied as she was disturbed.

Today it must be what they said.

Today we ate the rest of the game that we had had yesterday and with it mashed potatoes and after that there was a cake which is called Nelly which is very delicious.

Today we did not mind what she said when we were careful to avoid having been too often in their way. Today we were deeply impressed.

Today it might be that it was very advisable to like having a word with her.

Today she found it a pleasure.

Today also there is room enough and to spare. Today it might change from cotton wool to cotton that is to say that it might look like it without deceiving any one.

Today the same as yesterday there is not this difference in three Spaniards.

Yesterday we were invited.

Yesterday we accepted.

Yesterday we found it warm and rainy.

It was very easy to see veal to see veal.

Today to stay and having in the morning looked at birds.

Yesterday there was a lunch given and a salmon trout with women and men so that there was a host and hostess and four invited two as men and two as women. It was also a great pleasure to them that they not only had camellias but a camellia bush. Also a visitor who had lost what he had to have if he had been left to him. A disappointment.

The day before that a birthday and not a mistake.

The day before that the day after that they wished that Ada and Harry had had.

To never be behind that is what he said when Bertha can

be shortly changed from being strange to being whimsically inclined. Bertha is made of chairs, atlas and theirs. This sounds as if it were changed and it was.

Tomorrow she Helen will bring flowers perhaps.

Does she wash well. She washes well but it is difficult to say so because there is a criticism.

Does she wash well yes she washes well but it is difficult to say so because there is a criticism.

Does she choose meat well yes she chooses meat well but it is difficult to say so because there is a criticism.

Does she choose fish well. Yes she chooses fish well but it is difficult to say so because there is a criticism.

One two three times every day.

During these today three a weigh day.

There are more than three days passing passing with it be with it as fastening.

Helen bought no chicken.

Helen bought no chicken no Charlemagne no rhubarb and no more.

Every day was Easter. Easter Monday and Easter Sunday.

Every day they say that Indo-China is not far away.

We call.

This is after this after this a day.

Helen bought what she bought yesterday.

We bought three today.

To have pictures paid.

A rose tree may be may be a rose tree may be a rosy rose tree if watered.

Olga which is a Russian name gave us the rose tree just the same yesterday.

Rose tree a rose tree which is what is it oysters.

Oysters brown and rose tree rose he arose and he arose.

Watered and allowed makes a crown.

When Helen went home early on Sunday she did not remain as and because Monday would do just as well if not better.

What happened the other day. A natural dislike and in that they which is he resembled her which is why nevertheless and followed.

Yes in a way a guess yes. Three while one, Margaret Moll

Daniel Reagan Samuel Barlow. Three while one and one one will never remember if she was having carefully told all about Claribel. This is a day of happenings. They look out.

Helen did not buy for five what could be made to be four as will be left to that on the way in and on and about.

A diary should be simply be.

Yesterday hyacinths and anemones were under-foot at that. Yesterday at that.

Today having reproached an Englishman he was left. Today having reproached a frenchman and asked it to be when is it to more than to be so. Anybody who has been strangely left all together is mild.

Two days before that even in the evening it was not very much farther.

She did mind what they did.

Tomorrow she did mind having to do it.

Three days before preparation.

Bread can be kept endlessly.

He does think that if it is that that it is very serious.

He does think that if she has been with an admirably prepared advantage with him.

He does think that it is not extraordinarily recollecting everything.

He does think that she is a villainess and willing. A father when he is not a father can be encouraged. A son when he is not a son can be encouraged. A woman when she is neither a mother a sister or a wedding can be encouraged and so everything is regularly replaced.

This makes a diary.

Who is reputed.

This makes a diary.

Who has had whom.

This makes a diary too tenderly.

Yesterday we had a day in the country in which although there was wind and also a great deal of attractiveness nobody meant to have three gold watches which are two.

We were able to find a great many places where there were no lilies of the valley left.

It does not diminish if there has been no time in which to add it all. The majority do not care to have them young.

Who is as best as they know how. How many days are there in it.

The first day as much as seen.

That day was not mentioned.

The next day we met Tonny.

That was not mentioned because at that time we did not know that it would not be as merely if it was liked. It was so much liked that it has since been photographed.

Tonny could tell about having been mentioned and perhaps there are no more.

That is one day at most.

One day which is when it was fortunately Fania.

Fortunately Fania in every effect.

This day very much earlier not to have sat down.

Today having said that they were not desirable because they were in season having said that it might be that very well, all the time comes to be news.

Helen said that as it was Friday it was not possible to purchase pork.

And so be it.

As long as to best.

Yesterday was longer.

In the morning we went to see Cook's house and we were perfectly left behind by there not being having been being everywhere. What is the matter with it.

Next we came home and had had had been pleasing.

She made it do and it did very well it was very good.

After that it was very funny. Anybody can remember. It was very funny.

After that in the midst of after that a pleasant moment without without a pleasant moment without without without being without without having left just at once having left just at once without without he was without he was without it as we left.

After that by a miracle after that.

After that a long conversation about how many women are there about. After could it be that it would be natural not to be confiscated confiscated and confused makes of it an allowance. We came home we were very comfortable and this morning they were very practicably assigned to do it not as at once. We have decided to visit a cathedral when we wish. We wish that there could be a difference between twelve and half past twelve as they well may.

Pablo Picasso in photograph.

Olga Picasso as added as a wedding.

Paulot Picasso could rest upon his hand.

And after having been not liking a brother. Brother brother go find your brother.

This was a long day but presently.

Today.

Two days childishly.

Helen is not satisfied to have us ask them but we must.

Is which is ease.

Helen has to be told to buy artichokes even if she prefers to buy asparagus. Artichokes if she prefers to buy asparagus made in the fashion in which she has them made are not only healthier and more palatable but also more distinguished and if she is told so she will know so.

Nothing has happened today except kindness.

Today I will write to Elliot Paul and Bravig Imbs.

Today Belle and Marion will come not to stay but to eat lunch today. And we will be pleased to be nice to them in return for the kindness that has been shown to us by their husband but not by their father. We may have exaggerated it but there is some basis for it.

We will also think of something which might be done preferably today would have been admirably suited to go to Chartres which is a moderate sized city containing a cathedral although it had not been our intention to lunch in the town itself but at a certain distance from it where we have been told there is a great abundance of strawberries although not yet more than as tulips. The Johnstons having forgotten the Johnstons the Johnstons have brought us very delightful tulips grown by the daughter as she has an English Canadian mother whose uncle was connected with the stables in Italy of the mother of the country which is a way of saying Queen Victoria. It was Queen Victoria and she had a bench from which she could being seated rest as if arranged. We have frequently enjoyed it.

Making haste slowly might be everywhere Helen was not satisfied yesterday on account of taxes she said she would not continue to stay if they were given away.

Yesterday we turned hyacinths into wisteria.

Today we turned them back to hyacinths from hyacinths to wisteria.

Yesterday we had both ham and a fake bird. It can be very much enjoyed very much enjoyed. Today in the midst in the midst in the midst to know in the midst.

Today what could they come to do after a while.

Yesterday and today it was confirmed if they can remember they do do do so.

It is very pleasant to read a story that by the way is known by the way is shown by the way is coming to be dotted with little ways.

A diary means yes indeed.

Not to wish to mention that in return for kindness not in return for kindness.

One a day today it was an appointment I appointed it as not as much as if they could be having in general having it cold. And the reason was that it was a shock. And then deeply thinking it was a train a having in the middle the two and very many in four rooms and out of doors.

Helen was a disappointment in respect to veal but not in respect to not feeling it later as an instance.

Might any one eat unprepared grapefruit and do they.

Tomorrow Tuesday.

Tuesday having asked do they need to solder it they replied it is impossible because because of the vibration which would separate it one from another. Would separate it one from another. Also we had their notice. Also they not the ones not at once they were at once very obliging.

A distinct record of events. We went to a party and enjoyed it we had to seen at a distance the difference between early and in the middle with the prime minister also we had been prepared to take part in writing on stamped paper you do you do and afterwards as I say I was asked to speak and when I said we are not satisfied she was ill at ease not because of perfectly and yet just because of perfectly. Will they join the music.

White makes them exchange impressions of lilacs Judas trees mauve trees and wisteria. To return them to green and white naturally.

This is yesterday uninterruptedly as worn and as well.

Yesterday perhaps she was to be mistaken yesterday for yesterday as well.

Yesterday as well Mildred was certain that once in and they were in they would not get out once out. This she said and she was contradicted.

Very well in the morning very well Simon very well in the morning it was resembling very well hand-writing very well was resembling very well in the morning and in the evening when he came in he was without hesitation hesitating and very well he was intending to be standing and standing with a grain of sitting very well not hesitating but in making very well in making in attending in attention in attending as well as well very well. A diary should not be in writing.

Helen was dissatisfied with its being difficult and so it was decided that they would send some little one not twice a day not every day gradually gradually is out loud.

It is happily very pleasant to be surrounded by lilacs.

A happy widow without forethought. That is what she said with three eggs and much pleasure. Helen will be when Amelia will be when Amelia Helen will be when to prefer Helen Helen will be when to prefer Amelia Helen will be when. To remember that a diary is just as much as if they went away. At one time there was nothing to do.

And now. Beautifully sewed. And now beautifully beautifully sewed. An underskirt beautifully sewed by her. Beautifully sewed. And now. Beautifully sewed.

And now. Today today is celebrated in our annals by perfect satisfaction.

That was just the same as yesterday.

Today. Elmer today and the memory of Ulysses Grant and what he said about it to mean Grant.

Let us yesterday.

Poor dear René of whom we are very fond was here with Eugene who has to have to do to be to wedding.

Also a letter which promises to do good in the future to do good in the future if it is to do good in the future.

Also a letter which says that they felt well.

Also a letter to say that they are wondering will we be enthusiastic.

Also making it doubtful if Mrs. Belloc Lowndes is not right right as rain.

There has been no real rain lately.

Also to doubt.

We have gotten our list back.

Yesterday was a sad day.

Today a daisy day.

Today a pleasant day as she washed her hair.

Today is a pleasant day boiled beef tenderly boiled and roasted in the pot and very well surrounded by a particularly cordial expression of interest.

Today to sacrifice today.

Today as well as that.

Today to be passed in and about.

Every day up to today.

Then in and if in delicately painted. With this as hand at hand. Letting it be not only not only what we had but not an edging. So many things have been said so many times have it nearly pried pried open. Open sesame. That is with win win do. Let us say that from tomorrow to be interested in fried in butter.

So letting it be best.

Best and most.

Most and best.

Yesterday in window.

Today in having said it was in church. Tomorrow in their carriage. Today theirs having come. Yesterday petting it as if to stay away. Day before yesterday.

Let us begin a diary a diary of events.

This evening we will have not the first but the third asparagus.

A diary left on time.

Two came back one came here two came here three came here how many honeysuckles are there on it. Not at all the answer that they missed.

She was very well when we left her yesterday.

Today there might be a criticism as to glass as to chicken as to something else that was not completely mentioned. But in the meantime as in and out is less and less less and less more. More and door their successful wishes. We wish we had her and we have and we are very well pleased.

Josette and George, Virgil and Thomas John and Paul Alexandra and Allen Dorothea and Emily Marion and Michael a great many have been not only very much as much as but with them all.

In the meantime it will be why they wanted to have that.

With that it in with that it in in an organ.

Thinking in terms of a diary its origin and its nationality and its return.

A diary might be liked by them as it is what happens daily.

A diary might be very likely might be like as it is what happens daily.

A diary might be in with them as it is what happens daily. A diary as it is what happens daily. A diary of what happens daily is a diary having its commencement now.

What happens daily is that now there is no one who can sing.

What happens daily is that now there is no one who can sell apples as they are now finished. A diary of what happens daily is that it is warm today and that here it is very well meant when they are as if they were carefully told not tomorrow.

Every night on Monday.

Leave it to them.

Ida is very old and very cunning she is dissatisfied with not going.

Ida is not very old but very cunning she is satisfied that she is not going.

Emily can hear what is said when she is absent.

Dorothea is obliging and could be brought here.

Friday is sufficient.

And then after all we did not go and to say so with them at least which is no feast. Yesterday at last.

There used to be success and might have been with it all. We made a mistake in having attended and intended to ask them and this was to her to be of aid.

It is just as easy to make a diary of having asked her.

It is just as easy to make a diary of having asked for her.

Yesterday I was much impressed by having seen something that Jessie would have known as what happened. It was a quarrel and they were there and they were separated she would not have said so as they went away together. After all.

Politely at a time when conversation was not and navy blue.

Also Alvara Simon Guevara was permissible permissibly speaking.

It is a very sobering placed the d's at once and an S.

This is what makes Simon Simon there. In a diary they can feel so.

What happened today. To do and today. She says it is amusing but not a pleasure.

Helen has been impressed by a young man and Miss Sitwell.

An error is easily made between 1924 and 1925.

I said 1925 and I should have said 1924. This is because I made a mistake and beside that I was not able to remember and we all of us said 1925 and it was 1924.

Also they were able to be very happy about how much better it was to be different in detail if it was to that that they listened.

Today it is an advantage not to have done it in such a way that she would be delighted to ask me how many days have I been here when it is very cold for this time of year.

He is doing his duty which is an advantage because very well because very well very well very very well.

A diary should be instantly in recording a telegram. Also in

recording a visit also in recording a conversation also in recording embroidery also in recording having wished to buy a basket.
That is it.

How long ago between the show and the day after they had
gone away and it was not the same thing.

First they came in the afternoon and stayed a long time and
we told them that we would be glad to see them again.

Helen said she preferred that she should have ten visitors
rather than she should have one. She had one but that was not
Monday but Tuesday. However she was pleased that if we were
to have a duchess it should be a french one.

What can it be partly that it is not by this that we are shown
to be suspiciously famous. Afterwards which was the next day
we went to see Mildred and she was at length pleased.

Then since then since then as if I had not tried. And so forth.
Why is Harriet not pleased with two. Because two are one and
some. I dreamed that I had to explain that m and n are unusual
that is to say defendable. Very likely at the same time.

A diary can be likened to Israel Isaac and Jacob and their
customs to Bernard William and Charles and their customs to
Walter Emanuel and Robert and their customs to Osbert Elmer
and Elliot and their customs to Helen Dolly and Nathalia and
their customs. A diary of having heard Harriet had come.

Every day a little greeting from Virgil.

To return to a dogmatic diary.

Today we will try and do it either near the one where we
are or near the other one.

We have not been told today that she is pregnant but we
know it.

It is not very likely that it is true that Douglas is not only
not there but farther from that.

In this way and all around they are not my delight.

Let us begin as if we were living quietly.

What are we to do today. Helen had already gone to get
what he came to inquire about. This is the sort of thing that is
not disturbing but exciting and stimulating and makes it be fairly
theirs as they came. I like to be told not to go to the door. It is
very nice to have words and music and to see them at the same

time when by accident it is where they need it best. Most and best. France has very shortly the health of hope. Thank you for everything.

Should a diary be written on the morning of the day described or before.

Thursday and Wednesday.

Men women and children will try.

By and by.

It is not a very agreeable day and this is because it has commenced to rain and Helen has not been obliged to ask them not to come. In the meantime Helen has bought a salad. Otherwise nothing is necessary. We have spoken of the desirability of not wishing to go anywhere with not wishing to go anywhere with some one not wishing to go anywhere.

If hair is washed frequently it is very helpful to have me helping. Might it be mine. We also went to see Harriet last night and she was out that is to say she had not come in. Also in the afternoon we left what is ordinarily useful in the way of deplacing our individual attention from this to that and during the interval of waiting we went to see the flowers and it was said not passionately nor even with fervor but with ready attention that in preference of being additionally remembered peonies are preferred. As for me a diminutive peach-tree. Not only in respect to delightful fruit but also as to delightful foliage. We have invited not only Tzara but his wife to come day after tomorrow in the evening.

Let us leave a diary so that in referring to it it is very possible to know if any one had been present who might have been at all likely to find it sufficiently desirable to have it in time in order that it should not continue to be mysterious. In that way need him need him as one to be left to be known as not coming to be added to the occasion as it has been. This is the result of our having needed and liked it and meant it and have it.

Not being able to remember if when the Ford Madox Ford and so one does call him by his name and his name is his name just the same if they had been here if we had not been accustomed to Harriet she might religiously or in enlargement have not heard or been at it at once. Also if at most of the time it is because she meant and it was a cold rain this is another event to have on my left hand and of course on my right hand she is there. There where there where there there where. Besides that an opera should have been named gradually.

Helen's husband has cultivated two harvests of strawberries.

A diary should be only very reasonable an account of those who have been here.

Who have been here.

A diary might be met at a door.

A diary is not relieved from the necessity of lists of roses and peonies also of ribbon and attendance.

Has Bravig been here.

Yes.

Has Henry been here.

Yes.

Has Horace been here.

Yes.

Have we been here.

Yes.

A diary is as it were outstanding.

A diary of unusual occurrences and their resultant innovations. Today instead of writing in the morning or in the evening or in the afternoon or at once there has been perceptible delay and hesitation at a glance.

Day today.

Today not now and lightly. Wednesday if Monday has been left out.

Having not finished with John W. as who said who said who said he said. There are very pretty roses between the two below very pretty roses.

Helen has not ordered the beef à la mode and we are hoping that it is especially tender so that we will be able to say so. How pleasant it is to be able to think so.

Carl Van Vechten is pleased with Negroes not because they are different but because they are indifferent and not because of pearly teeth pearly teeth are only usual when when attribution is found to be made to it. Does Nora does Helen does Taylor does Rose does he do we do we abandon those who are wanted.

A diary should not go along.

A diary of hoping that we will still hear about the mill which may be satisfactory.

Underskirts can be religious.

Blue with green orange beige and a foundation of white can be left here.

They might prevent her from sealing but they do not everything can be attended to.

Does he does he do they do do they do they all to you all to you mine when they smile can you incline to be perfectly necessarily reminded.

Frank and Nelly Jacott finally said he finally said that they were not about to go to bed. In place gradually it was discovered that Arthur was not in any way satisfactory.

And then I was interrupted and after all I was interrupted and so forth.

Could it be asked why if they do not come come and go go and come why should it be intentional to be awake and say come to stay and she did. A diary is usually to be had at one time.

A diary is usually to be had at one time.

A diary is usually to be had at one time.

And a lamp between.

And not be seen.

And not to be seen.

And a blue queen.

Blue is the color of regularly.

A diary might be an instance of a border.

A diary of the knife cleaned upon which it said fight for your own country first. A diary of the chicken soup which can be mad[e] concentrated. Also a diary of singing it gradually as if they were not only not raining on Saturday but also on Saturday.

A diary of theirs at first.

A diary of the clock not having been not wound.

A diary also of adaptability.

Also a diary.

What is a diary to be. A diary is to be a diary of when this you see be all to me.

A diary not at all a diary of having a great many times not continued to be friends nor either a diary of what has happened to Elliot Paul.

A diary not a diary not a diary of this not a diary.

Will there be a diary a daily diary. There will not be a daily diary and this is because at that time naturally in order not to have it be as important as the other not at all.

HISTORY OR MESSAGES FROM HISTORY

(1930)

I have it to do.

They have it to do.

Lynn has to do it.

She is awake to bake cake.

Apart from a pie what can she do she cannot make a pie because she cooks a part of it separately and this should not be done for a pie.

The fruit in a pie should be cooked in a pie.

The pleasure of coming here is why they speak as they do. In this time they will manage not any longer to stay long to buy sugar as they have surpassed them as to their roses. This is how hours point.

We are no longer young in weather. It is very remarkable that we are very nearly perfect when we had been mostly troublesome. Now why. We do not know except that we were tired of meals in butter. Butter comes first.

The scene opens with a storm followed by rain but no hail. There was expected to be a wind storm. But even so there would be a little coldish air but not at present wind.

They were quietly expectant but a little irritable.

In a night it made no difference to it that it did not leave it which is it.

Do you feel well does he feel well. He is a little pale. Perhaps he needs more food. Perhaps he does. Then he will have it if it is what is when he has need of it.

She is very willing to prepare meals for him as well as for them unless it is raining in which case she is busy sewing.

There is no interest in regretting that they are equally regretting that it is a not as happy as for an occasion. This is why they are not here hardly why they mean this by threes.

He has not come back.

He is there and he has not come back.

Do they feel that this is their donation to lending, alas no, they are caught because they have won the right to be in meaning. I mean I mean was not said of women.

When made a link with then linked with men linked with a pencil or a pen linked with a pen wherein chickens are kept.

What is it.

A scene out of the window with the nightingales singing.

Beginning their singing which is intermittent at first.

Nightingales means nothing to those who have not heard them which many in America have not.

She wants to read it.

Lavender begonias heliotrope pinks roses and add pansies although they are not there but near give a great deal of pleasure in many ways.

Will it be that they will think with me. They will think it with me. They will readily be with me. They need to have it be here with me.

Five make forty-four we hope they will give us the house.

The house.

This house.

Not their house not his house it is her house but since she does not count it is a house. She does not need it it is not needed in place of usage.

Usage is when they made it do very well for the use of it.

It is very well that a little while they will have been happy to go.

It is indeed very desirable that in a little while they will have been prepared to have left when they did go.

It is not useful if they wait.

A little chicken does not prepare to step up. A little chicken is not little.

It is without eight pears.

They move about any men have pears to sell. Peaches are reasonable. Grapes are to be plentiful. Chickens are scarce.

You never can tell by their mistaking who lives in the house. A house is attached to others. By the time some have come.

Beans are peas. Placed so that they change with the weather. Nobody seeds which are washed away. They can be in and out of sight.

The dog looks young.

The colonel has directed the soldiers to grow nasturtiums. In argument.

A spinning of a tulip in a villa of lilacs is not magenta.

Attendance a necessity.

It is very easy to grow peas and be proud of a grandson and be fearful of the way he never passes.

Oh how can you bother with me.

They curtsied as they fished that is their father fished but not then.

Bob has a wife called May. She has lost her bloom.

Frank has a wife Diana who has a mother. She has a father who lives with the mother. She goes every day as they are not too far away.

Others have a friend who is not any longer able to care for them. They do still own them.

Nuns are made in their image.

A dog sleeps easily. There is very little variety he sleeps with variety.

It is useless both to remember names.

He comes running of which no one complains.

A dragging is made in bicycles. They will never forget women and bicycles, chickens and drawers and ebony and extensive burdens.

It happens that they will leave it with her and she will be happy to make more of it with theirs.

See how many changes make nobody lessen more days.

Now he there more for theirs.

This is never near by.

Again with their season.

It is why after me.

Letters are answered before us.

A little cup and saucer is of no use with dishes. Think of a reason for that.

How do you do if you make a mess.

It is regrettable to be sorry for them all. Think why.

AN INTERLUDE.

BEGONIAS.

Think with a minute, a minute is too baby who. An owl is a bird And wisely is furred Because it is true I love but you. She is winsome as a wicked nightingale. A nightingale means everything so does after music. Less is less than lest, lest we hear the nightingale. The meadow in which they throw rosebush roots is below. To refuse to be cajoled by in which. Oh thank you.

A name is normal they will be within reach of the sound that a name sakes for them they are awaked by the sound of their name which is spoken for reaching named it to them. They will be alike if they cannot get in. Houses are multipled with a hail storm. Cadence cup and ball. To matter in taming Bertha.

Climb into a coat. With them they are busy.

She is always right.

And beautiful.

Rested.

They will name arches by her. Leaves honey and lavender. Leave money for her finding it sunny. Money is a flower.

SYMBOLISM.

She means yes by yes and little by little and went there to have them along. Symbolism means yes by yes with part of it which they take. Taken made easily it is too bad.

I feel I know it now.

Without disguise although I am busy I have not to be assured where it is. All who call call with all their strength this not really so because they would be farther blamed as exhausted.

Let us think of symbolism in wading in a country where the water dries easily. It is a pleasure to find begonias although one does not care really to regard them because they will look well in the place in Versailles do you remember.

The characters are to be she and they. He is not dissatisfied. They are very well. It is very kindly. They are there where she is and that is because they will not be saddened by her living and leaving in three places.

One once with wedding made a glance with credit at once they made it a present to the ones they were with. It was known as attending to helping in accidentally never have to make it to them in their mistaken in what is the difference if it is or is not made on purpose when then it will do. The better wider that they mind after the firm of which they might be seated as if they had loaned it until they were through.

Nobody needs paper to make dolls with what they have for her. It is mine to idle and to chew which he would mean if he ran they were welcome as the difficulty of it all.

As breath of better instead of named when he heard her come not nearly as well as it was one and one.

One and one does he like to have to do it if not why.

There are so few that they will do.

Who has been here.

Once when I went I added three to we are here.

They went away and fastened it for me when this you see you are all to me.

In union there is strength they are after all to look for me.

When added as very likely.

They came and went and were heaven sent. Heaven is a place from which they are sent.

Well meant is when they come when they are invited.

These are the characters which emerge.

A dog has a heart which beats quickly when he is told.

They meant that old and gold and told are two words which resemble.

She made a discovery she asked who has been left to get it all.

If she married a general she was a widow. If she married an admiral she was a young girl.

In this way all the characters have come to be wealthy.

Wealthy and wise. We think that they are happy.

Happy is as happy does. They are very well when they have had a sister and a daughter. It is of assistance.

Now listen it is of assistance to them.

A moth in the moonlight is a moth indoors.

Joining is an amusement and a presence.

A lieutenant is not a captain in which way he finishes. I never like to think of anybody.

How many people have come home to attend to the little calves. One. She is to be with and with diminishes.

When she came today she said she would stay away.

No elephants are irritable as a sign.

One two three all out but she. A turk has held her by the hand, he has filled her heart and her hand and she is not displeased with money.

He is obedient in that way. She meant to like Thérèse. Thérèse is a sister she has a brother.

An african is not a turk he is an indian.

A hen is not a chicken she is an appointment which has been kept.

Who hurts him.

He hurts him.

Who will be welcome.

It will be welcome.

There will be an emigration.

They will have satisfaction.

Hours of their opportunities and they do not like to think about them. In this way they are selfish.

A happy hour.

Prefacing a happy hour.

It is untangible which means that the tangles have been taken out and there is a reason for their not gradually getting stout.

Maria Sera was her name there we do not know her name here.

Oh yes we will bless her we will be grateful and we may be left to be careless of how she does it.

A simple way of being here when she is obliging.

Now then.

Now and then François says he is all right Sunday and Monday. He says his father knows. He says he likes it all alike.

Anybody living here is in the fields and fearful not of thunder or of rain or of cold or of cows they are afraid of whether they will cut the hay.

PART II.

Play horses with oxen and copy carrots with seed.

She is just as well as that.

A mystery or Thérèse.

Why does not Thérèse have to go.

There is no mystery with the young man. He may not in fact it is said so he is not her son.

If they stand are they annoyed not if they are sitting they are annoyed not very.

It is easy not to have her crackle paper but not so agreeable. A dog sleeps he is not nervous when he sleeps.

A little noise is not attractive when it is made by her.

She moves slowly and works hard not to reach up but her boy is necessary to fail not her but his teacher who expect nothing better. She that is she in her letter said it better.

Better have sepoys than lovely ladies sepoys are hindoo soldiers in revolt.

There are two things that are interesting history and grammar. History is historical.

It is very well to like to have grammar. Grammar is acquainted with a way to feed them.

Think of history.

She made her have no hope of being married. That can never be history.

It was too bad that he was never hurried. That came [to] be historical.

Now she she being there and now always remembering the key to take the key there is no history in that. It is difficult to remember her. There is no history in that nor is there candy nor is there farming.

Abandoning grammar for history eating and farming and never being happy. She is very happy. He is very happy. He married the daughter of a dressmaker and she left to have a child by a cousin of whom she had been fond. He was a doctor and had been married to her. They will not be restless not her father and mother who have little dogs. They are not any stranger.

She likes a brown suit and a golden beard in a notary.

Anybody here is here for history.

An answer to where have you known of her is this I did not see her I bought it for her. This is not history.

Lands which are placed where they are forward and back and necessary and a little as late as ever is the history of whether they will be hurt by an accident. They can easily have their arm hurt but it does not hinder them neither their eyes.

In history one does not mention dahlias mushrooms or hortensias. They may mention tulips grasses roses and ducks and geese. They may mention dogs and geraniums and verbena also acacia lavender and apricots. Apples and pears and now birds and flowers and clouds and distance. History is placed where it is and hope is full of wishes. I wish to be with them. They are agreeable and fortunately able to like merry circuses. They appeal to the desire for weeding and patience. They make dresses prettily and wait. There is a difference between history and description. They will preface that. They have nieces for their vines. Vines which grow. They must be taken care of even if they fail to bear. This is not description it is not authority it is not history. The history of any opposition to happiness. There is no history in gentleness. She gently found mushrooms. She questioned the authority. It might have been many more there were quite enough. No history is proof against everything.

Moonlight in the valley is before and after history.

History of a lady whose grandchildren told her they were a king and she did not believe that he had come.

History of his making it be there were for them taken.

Little pay for places where they were rented to stay.

Knives cleaner knife cleaner.

Bed roses beds of roses bed of roses beds for roses roses are declared to have been chosen.

They chose or were chosen they chose roses or roses were chosen.

Beds for baking.

It is sideways to love having heard with them. Tomorrow.

Manage changes.

Leave it for babies.

Read it for changes. An annoyance.

Leave made maid for minding changes. They name by our changes. It is destroyed by happening to be with them. With them with him. Now think how is a history of think with them think with him think for him think for them think they were with him they thank and they thank him with them for him. Aloud is organized for louder.

How are ours meant for them in clouded. Rain is not accompanied by a sigh from dogs. Can they walk that way from tire. They are careful to be in the way by saving. Save. Like nine like welcome women. They must be chosen with them then they were worn with addition in meaning. It is so easy to confound her with the mother of little more than any more with them. They were outstanding in coining words without women. Leave it to me.

How could he be how little they like how many are there may be more names which they have by next to their home.

It is a passage where they were waiting. Who has a fancy for whom.

An entirely new way to say entirely.

I like horses to be with my father because he walks more easily with oxen.

That is it.

A pleasure to them all but why will they wait for me in regularly.

Leave it to be as much with intended women.

Names when they had named that.

Percy a prize.

Thank you for the surprise.

Lead ways are lost.

We will ask them to see to the light because it is of importance that we are obliging.

Finally with women.

PART II.

MESSAGES FROM HISTORY

Better than the mother she heard it be no bother.

Unless you look.

This is why he was not nervous but a little happy in their attention.

It is when they look that they look like that.

They expected thunder and they had rain and the thunder came after.

2

Love of a person makes better soften.

She made him like them.

It was not unwelcome to him.

They were repaid by them.

It is true that they give an account of it which is received with acclamation.

In the meanwhile do they have words with music.

Selfishly.

They account for it like this.

In union there is strength.

They were expecting it to be emphasized which whenever it was they know that they sided with intention with their impression nevertheless they were without choice which is where they were in repetition which they resettle alike in union there is strength and a hymn to have him be approached which makes it restless as after every little while they wait for it. An allowance for a cloud. It is bursting with rain the cloud is and it comes.

3

Shut up whatever you like with his being liked it is of no use that puppies and birds have little ones they have to respect it themselves. A pressure is that they have fought and told it about how they were wishing to be disappointing they make it be very much which they knew they had out right.

Leave winter to summer. That is what they do when they are within and without you.

3

How are errors avoided.

They are fresh as ever. He made it be that they are willing to mistake him for me. This is what is seen when they pass from one to one as they stand with their instruments in between not of farming not of fighting but of standing. And no one hears what they say. Why not if it is a word. Because they must not have known to more than those who like it. Everybody can be away for a minute. This makes all day easy.

4

Birdie is alike. Remain is alike and they nearly saw fog surround a cross. When they do this they in a little while buy something Swedish then all of a sudden there is thunder and this happens every once every hundred years.

5

Mainly being fine with willing to rain she is the one who has been right and right it is that it is never left to the judgment of one incapable to spell truly with the words behind which they make their treasure. She makes my happiness in every measure.

6

Birds make religion this is known every hour and why because it does not belie what she cherishes. She cherishes me so tenderly. They will be thought best and most and she is all.

7

The lesson of history so she says is that he will do it again but will he we hope not.

8

A famous wife is married to a famous poet both beloved. This is what history teaches.

9

What is history. They make history.

10

History is this.

Human nature is the same that is not history.

A dog is dissatisfied and restless that is not a history.

He is unpleasant in all his little ways and we do not care about him although we forgive him that also is not history.

The son of Mrs. Roux has failed in his examinations that is to say he has been discouraged from attempting them that is not history.

What is history they make history.

In times of attention they are not certain that they will obtain what they wish this might be history but it is not history.

Intention is not history nor finality finality is not history. Think what is history.

Mildred made and knew history.

Pierre does not make but fears history.

Bernard leaves and leans on history.

Once upon a time a couple had a dog who aroused universal admiration.

They were by nature interested in antithesis. They followed when they came they were much in use and equally they were amused. They were not behindhand with arguments in their arrangement there were birds who had built a nest who unable to be in that place might have come in and out, and puzzled the dog. They were imaginative they hoped for the best and they had seen that chickens can die and be complained of. It was very often inconsiderate to not be found noisily precious to their employees. Leave well enough alone was never said by them. They amounted to that. There is a difference between noisily and visibly so they thought and they were attacked by those who found them wanting in delicacy of expression. It was not often that they were disappointed, they were alike in being often weather beaten.

Who makes it be incompatible with fame.

It is terrible when weather is not propitious.

In time they were accustomed to sunshine they had been accustomed to sunshine and they were tired of it sunshine accompanied or unaccompanied by wind, they were a little at a time desirous of mountains in the distance and one at a time they were recognized. They were very often coming to be an outstanding responsibility to those who were not careful. When any little arrangement was made they were not very careful and yet without abundance they were quite careful. They were astounded in accordance with the establishment of an adventure. In various times they were subject to prophecy. In all it was part of a reason.

Very often any date could be in amount without counting. In hopes and in all their objection to invitation they were obliging they were sweet they were attractive and attracting and an allowance being made for what they considered wholesome and injurious they were very often wilful a subject is varied by their achievement. In every little while all pieces of renewing and there they might be doubtful of a choice and their habit would be not seized but reluctantly and therefore consciously to remind leaving, it was as of no occurrence lending for them was a pleasure and yet it could be refused not the pleasure but the organization. It is not often that two people agree about having had it all. In this way it is a little changed.

Abruptly thinking is not a surprise they may be blamed because in a pleasure there is always a rejoinder. How do you like your favorite scent.

If you say you prefer pansies that may be because of delicacy. Pansies are pretty.

They went away and they had in common that the present

and at present they are careful made it be by means of altercation that shouting is heard at a distance this may be conversation. What is history.

History is the learning of spectacular consistency privately and learning it alone and when more comes they receive.

5

Do be asked to bag grapes.

Do be asked to make grapes into raisins.

Do be asked to bag grapes so that they will not come to be raisins.

6

History pleases when will for their sake they repay their adage.

Bay is a bay with a lake.

7

History is this they may I say add leave that.

8

Jacob pays Marcel who saw Francis leave wood for wages.

His heart is like a lion by reason of the muscle in his arms down to his hands.

9

The mother of Bernard and Florence had a little boy which they left is this what is bad for history no because it is funny. It is not history by a viaduct. She need leave she leaves with a relish for resting which she had. A viaduct brings water not milk water in abundance is bad for wheat, wheat is not wholesome. Butter is and so is food. She eats food.

History rests by this they mean they make history all day a dog will come when he is called and go away, this is history because a dog does not fare as well there as here. A dog is in hope of learning a mountain and a mountain is helpful in being called for them. They will manage it better.

9

What is history. Leave leaves and summer. Lettuce leaves and spring and summer. Leaf when an officer marries a daughter and they will have a home together. A leaf of embroidery. She makes leaves and a leaf very perfectly making it with a better than hopefully. Hope was in praise of hoping. This is the history of a name.

10

Beware of a lake the sun may shine and the reflection burn you or it may be cold either way is as it were a frontier. A frontier is a division between countries. A history of a country is not a history of the changing of frontiers although many think so particularly those near the frontier the history of a country is why they like things which they have and which they do not exchange for other things for which they do not care. They have a particle at a time of any more and they are never eager. No country is ever eager.

This account is one which makes no account of waterfalls or trees or any ground which is used for giving them this. They are not acquainted with any one who has butter for sale. There are many ways of drowning bees in honey those used in a country are the same anywhere.

Hours of clouds.

They like to gather what they plant.

11

Bakers bake in February.

Thank you.

12

April is fully a holy day too
A holiday for a shoe.

12

Pink blessing is helping heard them make it do.
She is established with having it for you.

Little as well as do.

14

What is history he felt that it was not a foolish thing to do.

15

HISTORICAL

Flowers	7	And lovely flowers mostly roses pansies and dahlias.
Herbs	7.15	And very delicate and spicy herbs.
Francis	7.30	He was quite welcome was he not.
Hat	8	A hat very well suited to the usage for which it was and is intended.
Beans	9.30	A great many beans.
Basket	10.30	He is sometimes a trial of patience.
Bathe	11.30	A pleasure and a refreshment.

This is historical in the best sense.

16

History teaches us that whether clouds have in the part of them a spiral movement made by the action of the wind or not as long as the barometer shows no change the rain will continue, at intervals, with pleasant weather interspersed.

17

History is this. He is not happy because he is worried by his refusing to be able to have his hopes succeed rapidly one after the other not that he has hopes to fulfill but he has hopes which follow all the while there is great bitterness because he goes when he does and he comes as he does and he does nothing without refusing such as has been asked of him. This you can see sounds historical and in a way it is historical. It is not his history it is historical thank you very much.

18

Leaves of history.
If they smile at a photograph taken of them in the sun.

19

What is history. They make history. Just why do they like birds seen in the way he saw them it was very pretty and made it be very welcome in the telling.

20

If they send it to him as well as to her both will have had it.

If they do this for both of them either of them will be the one to tell the other.

The way to taste is to be welcomed as eating.

Any acquaintance with their having had it is nullified.

And in indemnifying them for awaiting the disadvantage of their reason.

The history of satisfaction.

She ate late because she had had to wait.

He is ready to leave but he must wait until they are after all not to wait.

It is better that they should all wait. They wait.

It is now time that they had come to go having waited.

They are able to wait but they would as leaf not wait. Having waited they would rather after all not wait.

They will go together that is they will leave none of them behind.

21

What is history it does not leave dogs for cows. It does not will not please not, an opportunity not to call when they are after the interval known that they may be perfectly left for them in a place.

22

History, it is said so kindly she ate the pear not the whole but the top of a pear which being a favorite morsel had been delicately offered and the offering is not in vain as it has been as much known.

Do think things.

23

Behavior pleases many. His behavior leaves nothing to be desired by any one coming into any contact with him he is pleasant and ferocious he can see with what he likes when they call officious a farewell to society and also he never has been referred to as being with them there in the meanwhile it is as when they must must she come she came and left with it as attached to attach left where they went he was on the place with what they asked of pleasing.

It is mine to ask plenty of them to go away.